From Caterpillar to Butterfly

Beyond all illness, ailments & disease

Iris Sparkes

Published by

MELROSE BOOKS

An Imprint of Melrose Press Limited
St Thomas Place, Ely
Cambridgeshire
CB7 4GG, UK
www.melrosebooks.com

FIRST EDITION

Cover designed by Richard Chambers

ISBN 978-1-906561-51-2

FSC
Mixed Sources
Product group from well-managed
forests and other controlled sources
Cert no. SGS-COC-2953
www.fsc.org
© 1996 Forest Stewardship Council

Printed and bound in Great Britain by:
CPI Antony Rowe, Chippenham, Wiltshire

Acknowledgments

At the outset, thanks must go to Ann and Gerald Garrard for their very useful comments and assistance. Also grateful thanks to my daughter Gillian, for her thoughts, suggestions and support.

Finally, a thank-you to everyone at Melrose Books who has helped everything to come to completion.

Foreword

Iris Sparkes came into my life the day after I wrote a letter to God asking for guidance and health (ask and it is truly given).

As a friend, healer, meditation teacher and inspiration she has supported and guided me all the way on my journey from ME to "true" health with healing, wisdom and on-going support.

Since our meeting I can say with the utmost confidence and belief that I have the best and most effective healthcare in the world. I often tell friends that the greatest gift I could give them is Iris' card and telephone number.

This book will be a great step in "waking up" the world to the direction healthcare will take in the 21st Century.

Thank you Iris for all you have done and carry on doing for me and my family.

Neil Allamby
A house father and husband

For my family
Twin soul
... and all the ageless spiritual inspiration

"Let's give everyone a three-hundred-year life. It will be the biggest event since the creation of man: it will be the liberating and creating anew of man! God, what man will be able to do in three hundred years! To be a child and pupil for fifty years; fifty years to understand the world and its ways and to see everything there is; and a hundred years to work in; and then a hundred years, when we have understood everything, to live in wisdom, to teach, and to give example. How valuable human life would be if it lasted for three hundred years! There would be no fear, no selfishness. Everything would be wise and dignified. Give people life! Give them full human life!"

'The Makropoulos Secret'
the celebrated play by Karel Copek

Introduction

This is a book about human beings in transition from our present state to visions of ourselves never before experienced, much like the caterpillar that becomes the beautiful butterfly, spreads its wings and flies – seeing vistas only dreamed of. We are changing into a new species which, like the metamorphosis of the caterpillar, is happening in silent unseen ways.

This is a book about how I have become aware of all this through my own personal experience; by no means the only journey, for many paths, like many little rivers running into the ocean, eventually create the larger picture of life.

Step by step I seem to have been preparing for the development of rather unusual healing abilities whereby, through the name of a person, I can read their health state and what they need in order to help the body to heal itself naturally. This may sound implausible but we are learning through quantum science that our whole world is nothing other than vibrating energy at different frequencies and therefore the name a person uses has a very unique vibration too. This is why, if people change their name, like women at marriage, it in some way alters the vibrations around them.

This is also a book that talks of the meaning of life and how human beings fit into it all, drawing on the healing experiences of my growing number of clients and through the regular checks which afford me a unique opportunity to observe everything.

Finally I offer glimpses of what we human beings might experience once we are able to overcome the limitations of the caterpillar, spread our wings and FLY.

Chapter 1

"We come spinning out of nothingness,
scattering stars like dust."

Sufi poet Rumi

This is my story of how I've reached this point in my life – a minute fragment in the long history of the evolvement of us human beings.

As a child, I suppose I was a bit of a loner, "away with the fairies" as they say, until I realised that I wasn't quite living up to the expectations of my mother. "Achievement" loomed large over my life. Schooldays were memorable for one thing – the lack of anything that might be called academically pleasing – for my mother, more than my father, had high ambitions for her eldest daughter. Unfortunately, these were never fulfilled according to her expectations. The "coup de grâce" came when, at just 21, I made what she considered to be a disastrous choice of marriage partner. Four children and many years later I emerged from my very rewarding role as a full-time mother to dip my toes into the outside world! What did I know most about but children? So I became a playgroup helper. Although this involved much organisation at home, I managed to do a weekly course at Morley College in London and despite almost dropping asleep by the afternoon session, this enabled me to start my own playgroup.

A year after getting the playgroup off the ground my husband was re-located to the North of England where I quickly became involved with taking over another playschool. I became actively involved in the local Branch activities and was appointed as the first Area Organiser looking after all the other playgroups in the district. After many rewarding years I then felt it was time to move on, so I applied for the post of and was appointed as the Manager of the local Citizens Advice Bureau. It was fascinating work and I loved it!

Chapter 2

S uddenly, out of the blue, like a thunderbolt, I was profoundly affected by a man who crossed my path. This flung me from the surface of life to the very depths in ways that I had never experienced before. Obviously it was not intended that any relationship develop but nothing has ever been the same again for the memory of that experience continues to weave its threads into my life in ever more meaningful ways. This was many years ago now, and when my husband and I eventually separated, I chose to live alone and have been very contented for no other relationship could ever be really satisfactory. At the time I struggled to keep going with the daily routine at home and at work. My comfort at that time was to read and read like never before, to try to gain more and more understanding of what life was all about. Searching through a bookshelf at this time *"The Prophet"* by Kahlil Gibran, a Lebanese Poet, more or less fell out and I recalled words spoken by the first National Adviser to the Playgroup Association, a lovely lady who had impressed me a lot at the first conference I attended of the Playgroup Association. When reflecting on children this was the very book she had quoted from! It contains lovely little facets on life, a gem of a book. So many times over my life I've quoted from *"The Prophet"*, especially the fragment on pain.

"Pain is the breaking of the shell that encloses our understanding."

I then remembered other words she had said: 'We start from where we are.' So, I didn't in fact have to understand everything in one go and this was a great comfort to me too.

In astrological terms I am a Taurean. Taurus, the Bull, is an earth character and it is well known that "cows like to sit down and chew the cud". We are patient people and are also considered to be emotionally strong, probably a great strength at the time. It is said that when the student is ready the teacher is at hand. At school one is told <u>what</u> to think not <u>how</u> to think.

On my quest I discovered that many people had things to say that went way beyond just information. I started to realize that acquired knowledge is finite but beyond the thinking mind there is a very different place that really knows. I heard about a local Theosophy group where certain subjects were discussed in depth. Theosophy was founded in 1875 and looks at the sacred writings of Brahmanism and Buddhism, new non-western ideas for me to ponder. This extended my perceptions further and was instrumental in my first hearing about the practice of meditation, a process that leads to relaxation, peace and integration, through personal experience. This was quite different to the acquired knowledge of religious beliefs, although I had felt really at home attending High Church with my parents every Sunday; I loved the ritual of candles and incense. This was to come full circle when, a few years later, I was introduced to the British Meditation Society where candles, incense, flowers and fruit are used as part of the initiation rituals. I understood how important it was to learn correct meditation and spiritual practices from a trained meditation teacher. This has had a lasting effect on my life for I have been teaching meditation myself now for over 20 years. For five years I attended retreats and listened to words of wisdom from one of the world's great spiritual teachers, Gururaj Ananda. The contemplative side of religion now seems to have been lost in the Western lay traditions.

Three valuable books on the teachings of Gururaj are *"The Path of Unfoldment"*, *"From Darkness to Light"* and *"The Master Reflects"*. He "died" to this dimension in 1988.

Chapter 3

"While Eeyore frets... and Piglet hesitates... and Rabbit calculates... and Owl pontificates... Pooh just Is."

"The Tao of Pooh" by Benjamin Hoff.

"Meditation brings us nearer to the truth than anything else."

Before anyone embarks on the three month course I teach, I always invite the person to an introductory talk so they can decide if it is what they are looking for. There are many different forms of meditation since it has been around for thousands of years. Anybody can learn to meditate. It gives the ability to "change what can be changed, accept what can't be changed and the wisdom to know one from the other". There are many reasons why people seek meditation but it is mostly a search for happiness. Through meditation we learn that happiness is WITHIN.

When we talk about turning within, it is because we are more than just mind and body. We have a spiritual aspect as well. A good analogy would be a coconut. The outer shell, the soft inner part and then, finally, the milk in the centre. We know quite a lot about the outer and inner parts of ourselves but the deepest aspect cannot be KNOWN but only EXPERIENCED. This is probably one of the reasons why we have not understood a lot about this aspect, especially here in the Western World. In the East there has always been a disposition towards contemplation. This inner contact through meditation leads us towards all intelligence, creativity and love. Ignorance veils our true nature.

When we incarnate into life we weave inner layers, known as subtle bodies, which finally emerge as our physical body. We are literally spirit having an earthly experience. This spirit is the individualised aspect of what might be termed God/ Source/ Universal Spirit/Universal consciousness. When we turn our <u>attention</u> inwards it is rather like entering a perfume factory; we just need to go there to come out smelling of scent!

We rapidly discover the benefits of regular meditation. On the <u>Objective level</u> physical health improves for dis-ease is to do with fragmentation and lack of integration. On the <u>Mental level</u> problem solving becomes easier, intuition and concentration improve. At the <u>Heart level</u> we become more caring and loving towards others and relationships improve. Negative feelings are replaced by positive thoughts. At the <u>Deepest level</u> we gradually reach a state of awareness and consciousness where belief or faith becomes knowing. "Meditation is the highest form of prayer." We come to realise that spiritual growth is the purpose of life. As human beings we have, to use an analogy, put ourselves into plastic bags full of water, forgetting that the water all comes from the great sea. We gradually come to appreciate how we obviously must need more than just one lifetime to perfect ourselves which is the basis of the understanding known as reincarnation.

At the end of the three month preparation course students are given their individual mantra. This is the original sound, emanated at the very beginning of the soul journey, and which is picked up and given back to the person. It is in harmony with them and as personal as a fingerprint.

Meditation is very much a self-help technique. However as soon as we take one step forward, Divinity takes ten steps towards us. Growth and change are gradual and rarely take place in a straight line at a steady pace. A real Spiritual Master is a channel a bit like a switch on the radio we press in order to hear the music. The human being needs the personal touch but Gururaj made it very clear that once we discover our own Higher Self the work of the Spiritual Master is finished. As he said, "The teacher shows you the path, but you have to walk down it on your own two feet. There is no other way. No one else can evolve you, you have to evolve yourself."

After teaching meditation over a long period of time I know how very important it is to have a teacher, for checking sessions are the way the student and teacher can appreciate how things are going for that individual. We do need help to start off on the path and many people have said on coming to me that they have tried to meditate alone without success.

After the initial six weeks which is essentially a time to relax the body, other techniques are then given, for the body and mind are so closely linked. TRATAK is a technique 5,000 years old for grounding and the development of inner awareness and visualisation. It counterbalances the expansion of the consciousness with the mantra. Words used are from one of the oldest languages, Sanskrit. Through this Tratak practice a hormone known as Melatonin is secreted which rejuvenates the whole glandular system. As we shall see, I believe the endocrine glandular system is the key to the evolvement of humanity as a species. It is the level at which I focus all my current healing work.

Laurence Gardner, a Fellow of the Society of Antiquaries, an intellectually renowned sovereign genealogist and historical lecturer, Knight Templar of St Anthony and the appointed Jacobite Historiographer Royal, has written a number of books including *"Bloodline of the Holy Grail"* and *"Realm of the Ring Lords"*. He discusses the mystery around the legendary powers and miraculous potential of a substance called "White Powder Gold" in a book published in 2004 entitled *"Lost Secrets of the Sacred Ark"*. This substance aims to have a similar effect to meditation on the endocrine glandular system. However, wise people warn that humanity cannot force evolvement without dire CONSEQUENCES!

After the Tratak practice two further practices are given. The first one is an important breathing practice with a specific ratio to bring the individual into alignment with the breathing of the Earth. The second is a specific practice to link the meditator into the universal spiritual energies that saturate the whole universe and which form seventy percent of our spiritual evolvement. At the end of three months, when the individual meditators have practised all the techniques regularly and feel ready, they receive the individual mantra which replaces the temporary mantra. This is given in a special little ceremony. The individual now begins the journey of evolvement.

These are some lovely words from an Old Persian text:

"God sleeps in minerals
Dreams in plants
Stirs in animals
Wakes in man."

Chapter 4

"Healing is a journey the client embarks on, not a procedure the Healer performs. It is a broader, more global and complete approach – for healing is nothing less than an awakening to a vision of our healed nature and the experience of infinity."

"Shaman Healer Sage" by Alberto Villodo

Perhaps I am fortunate in that by nature I am quite self-disciplined, so I was quite happy to continue the practice of meditation on a very regular basis, twice a day, day after day for years, not having any particular expectations.

It was probably quite a natural step to proceed to spiritual healing. In the British Mediation Society people didn't come into healing until they had practised meditation for many years, in my case nearly ten years. It is considered that one needs these years of purification before the Universal Healing Energy can flow from Spirit, through the healing intermediary, to the spiritual aspect of the person to be helped. The healing practitioner is not involved at all in how or where healing takes place; only Divinity knows where it is needed through this act of Grace. And so healing can be received in quite different ways to those one might expect.

Much of what is considered to be spiritual healing is, in fact, magnetic healing where healers direct their <u>own</u> energy and although temporary relief can often be experienced symptoms can break out elsewhere, at a later stage, in another form, rather like curing a headache which surfaces again as a toe ache. Many healers practising in this way eventually experience a deterioration of their own health with severe depletion of energy. And, of course, unless practitioners are integrated in mind, body and spirit their own imbalances can be passed over to the client, exacerbating problems. This is not the way things should be at all for there is so much misunderstanding of the nature of true healing as taught by the great spiritual teachers. It is definitely a weakness in the Western way of proceeding to think that attending courses and acquiring knowledge and information confers on people the level of consciousness and understanding to practise things! Medicine as an art form has gone astray and unless we are very careful complementary therapies will make similar mistakes as vulnerable people search desperately for answers to their health issues.

Chapter 5

"All of life is a lesson in Self-knowledge."

"The Camino" by Shirley Maclaine

Having the solid foundation of meditation and healing it then seemed interesting to explore Homeopathy, Colour Therapy and Shamanism which have all contributed to my current unique healing approach.

It was about this time that I first noticed an interesting advert in a health magazine, "Does your body need an M.O.T?" This intrigued me, for yes, mine might well do! I had been following a new diet for a number of years and I was beginning to wonder whether it really was right for me. This was the start of a complete move away from orthodox medicine to homeopathy. I had had various ongoing health issues and the practitioner who had written the advert was quite unique in his field. He was developing a "consciousness to cure" approach which appealed to me. Gradually I learned more and more about how the unseen multidimensional energy fields around the body affect the physical body. Unless all these layers are in a state of balance, illness and disease will inevitably occur at some point. These layers are known as Mind/Body/Spirit and all vibrate at different frequencies in much the same manner as the different stations on our TVs and radios transmit on different wave lengths. This is quite a good analogy, since no equipment would work without correct invisible electrical waves and the Mind, Body and Spirit also need to resonate in the appropriate way.

Homeopathy is considered by many to have the greatest potential to affect even the most subtle layers of the body's energy fields. It was discovered by Samuel Hahnemann in 1790 after a long search for a safe and effective means of treating patients. There are over 3,500 remedies available now which are derived from all sources, plants, animals and minerals. These are available in the form of tablets, pills, granules, powders and liquids at different potencies which are at different levels of energetic effectiveness. They work rather like peeling off the layers of an onion, to reach the cause of the problem.

Colour Therapy was another subject I became interested in. I was also thinking about my future after I had finished working at the C.A.B. I did courses and obtained a Diploma whilst still working full-time. This was a very important step for, as part of diagnosing for colour treatment purposes, we were trained to use the pendulum for dowsing. This is an ancient art used mainly for detecting water. I prefer to call it "divining" as it used to be called, for one actually tunes into one's Higher Self/Soul, the all knowing part of oneself. I had known I could do divining quite early in my life but didn't explore it much whilst the children were young. I was too busily occupied!

Now I had found a focus. Colour therapy can be given in various ways. Perhaps the most widely known about is Chromolight where coloured filters are used to give people a treatment. Another technique uses Silk Scarf applications. Visualising colour is another approach and yet another technique uses food.

Personally I have found the most effective way has been a small chromolight box with a perspex top where I place the required colour filter. I put the picture of the person to be helped inside the box which I then leave on the window sill in the light and, by the transfer of colour rays, the person receives the colour healing. This box was created by my colour tutor and although it seems to work "by magic" it is actually a process that science has now started to explain for we now know that life forms are in fact bundles of energy vibrating at many different frequencies. These frequencies also make up the colours of the rainbow which, as some of us may remember from our school experiments, are in their turn the constituents of White Light.

Natural therapists seek to help a person's body to re-harmonize in much the same way as we retune a musical instrument. As we shall see, the retuning needs of people are highly individual, a fact that is not often really understood by many practising therapists. In the early days of colour healing treatment I myself was mystified as to why I failed to get a response to a specific treatment for everybody and I began to observe this by keeping records. Eventually I came to understand that every person is at a different stage in the healing process. However, when we start to walk down this path we move further and further away from a system in which the same symptoms receive the same treatment. As time has gone by I have also realised that the truth of any situation can only be understood according to one's level of consciousness.

I learnt a lot from Dr David Hawkins PhD and his book *"Power vs Falsehood"*. Kinesiology is another way of obtaining information, often used for example in allergy testing. Nevertheless David Hawkins, rather like me, has developed his own approach. I will return to him later.

By this time, on the personal level, my husband and I were living separately. This opened up more opportunities and I was drawn towards a sacred journey to Peru. I had the opportunity to accompany Leslie Kenton, the well-known writer on health issues and a Shamanic teacher. It was the first time I had explored Shamanism and it fascinated me. It is a tradition that goes back thousands of years and the ancient Inca healing techniques are still known high up in the Andes away from religious persecution. In 1993 I discovered a book about these teachings – *"Shaman Healer Sage"* – by Alberto Villodo, and about his 20 years of living high up in the Andes with the descendants of the Inca tradition. Villodo deserted a promising career as a Scientist and Medical Anthropologist to learn more about this tradition.

I decided to explore integrating this knowledge into my own healing work after discovering new things quite unexpectedly through my own self-healing. I extended these techniques to other people known to me and I was able to observe the results on them. I found it had an effect on the bloodline ancestry. This was the first time I realised something profound was happening, something at the level of Karmic "release"!

Karma is an Eastern word for the universal law, more commonly heard in the saying "As you sow so shall you reap". It teaches us how families reincarnate backwards and forwards into the same group, lifetime after lifetime, because of unfinished business that has gone on and on for aeons. A sort of re-cycling although the roles of each individual change every time they reincarnate.

So what is Shamanic knowledge all about? Well, it has derived from one of the oldest religious belief systems known to humanity, going back as far as the early Stone Age. According to Michael Harner who has practised shamanism and shamanic healing for more than a quarter of a century and written the book, *"The Way of the Shaman"*, first published in 1980, it is a great mental and emotional adventure, one in which the patient and the Shaman healer are both involved. Through his heroic journey and efforts, the Shaman helps his patients transcend their normal, ordinary definition of reality. Personal power is fundamental to well-being and the Shaman is able to help others who are weak, ill, or injured because he or she has the advantage of being able to move between different states of consciousness.

Jeremy Narby, in a book written in 1995 and translated into English in 1998 called *"The Cosmic Serpent: DNA and the Origins of Knowledge"*, writes, "People who practise Shamanism know about the hidden unity of nature, because they have accessed its <u>reality</u> by intuitive means and much of what has been said for thousands of years is now being confirmed by molecular biology." Jeremy Narby criticises today's science when he says "Biology has become an industry that is guided by a thirst for marketable knowledge rather than by ethical and spiritual consideration."

Although I don't actually practise the Shamanic techniques, having access to this ancient knowledge allows me deeper understanding of the causes of illness and disease and the healing levels needed for my clients. In a meditative state I simply "ASK" and the renewal process begins for the person concerned, acting in the entire context of the individual. "Ask and it is Given" is a law of the Universe but we need to have a certain level of consciousness before we gradually come to fully understand this law.

All this knowledge began to align with my studies with the British Meditation Society of ancient wisdom taught for thousands of years and which now forms part of my meditation course.

Impressions of all experiences over aeons of time are stored as vibrational imprints in the subtle body associated with the Chakra System which sits between the interface of the subtle and physical body. The Chakras, also known as vortices of energy, are very much affected by our thoughts and feelings and are linked to the endocrine glandular system in our physical bodies.

We are governed by a blueprint of issues we have agreed to address prior to each incarnation. It is like a dormant computer programme that, when activated, "compels us through behaviours, relationships, accidents and illness". So perhaps now we can begin to understand how very complicated our lives can be! It has been described as being beautifully set-up for us all to evolve. Quantum physics is altering the view of traditional scientists to a more unifying perspective of our universe. Western trained doctors, like Deepak Chopra, have left orthodox medicine to work in a more holistic way involving Indian Ayurvedic medicine.

Francis Thompson the poet expresses this beautifully:

"All things
By immortal power
Near or far
Hidden
To each other linked are
Thou canst not stir a flower
Without troubling a star."

Western medicine, although it advances in some areas, can never really succeed until it moves away from just treating the symptoms which mostly comes down to papering over the cracks! We need to look at human beings in their totality. Why do acute cases reach that stage in the first place? When one thinks about things in the light of what has been said we easily come to the conclusion that a large number of medical techniques have had to develop due to misunderstanding and neglect at earlier stages of the health issue. We thus come to a point where it is not unreasonable to describe drugs as being strangers in a foreign land where everyone else can speak the language except them.

And yet the body seems equipped to heal itself given the correct support. Bio-chemists tell us that the human cell is programmed to live for at least 120 years so if we "die" before this it is not from old age!

Chapter 6

"Everyone acts from his own level of awareness...
we simply act as our level of consciousness dictates."

"Creating Health" by Deepak Chepra MD

I was starting to move into very new fields of discovery. Perhaps my long years of practising the purifying meditation and spiritual techniques were now bearing fruit. A meditation student asked me to review a tape on a company marketing nutritional supplements. I was very impressed by the quality of the products and the network marketing ideas so I became an agent myself. The project involved investigating the link between health and spirituality through nutrient supplements by using the divining technique. This was to be the beginning of my own current unique health explorations. What began as a fairly small study was extended to hundreds and hundreds of people, known and unknown to me, ordinary people, well-known names, celebrities, and the palette was very wide. It was very interesting to study people I didn't know personally as clients, and who were therefore not taking the necessary supplements.

At the end of 2003 my homeopathist, whom I had been working closely with by this time – feeding reports back to him - had suggested I study the endocrine glandular system since it is so closely associated with the chakras and our life blueprint. I have gradually observed the importance of the endocrine system. This has proved to be the focus of my current healing work, for the endocrine glands, when balanced, are the key to the health of the body, a fact not unknown by the orthodox medical profession. Bringing together all my studies I was able to look at how the endocrine system becomes depressed and out of balance. I now needed more people as clients in order to study the healing process in action and this came about in an unexpected way.

Whilst talking to a homeopathic vet about remedies that might be helpful to my son's sick little dog, I said to her, 'Although I'm not a homeopath if you suggest a few things I will look to see what is beneficial to him personally', to which the vet replied, 'Could you also do this for me?' – Well, actually 'Yes', and from that, by word of mouth, my abilities have started to spread because what is also perhaps unusual is that I can do all healing work at a distance. Distance is of no consideration. My clients now come from all over the country and some of them even come from abroad.

It has taken time to decide what to actually call myself – this year it is between "Health Intuitive" and "Body Whisperer"; this latter was suggested by an original client, meditator, and now a close friend.

Chapter 7

*"Help thy brother's boat across and lo thine own
has reached the shore."*

Hindu proverb

So how do I work on a day to day basis? Well, after listening to the reason why the person has contacted me I explain how I work and how they personally might benefit. I then tell them I'll ring back and discuss the issues before proceeding to do any healing work. I do not do any healing "distance" or "hands-on" until the client is happy about this. Very often there are changes following healing. A supplement originally discussed needs to be changed, or possibly it is needed in a different amount or for a different length of time. All this is reported back. At the end of the process I explain how I continue to do re-checks, contacting the client when any changes occur and inviting the client to contact me at any time if necessary.

So, at this preliminary stage I look at the state of the client's endocrine glandular system. In most health issues this system is depressed and I then search for causes. One of the first things I look for is "spirit attachment" which is a much more common issue than people may think. This is not really understood by us here in the Western world although it has been understood in ancient cultures for thousands of years. When a person "dies" they mostly do not go to where they should, that is, the higher realms. Confusion takes place at death whereby the "entity" feels safer remaining "attached" to a living person. This confusion is exacerbated by death rites not being handled very well in the western world which especially applies to the Roman Catholic ritual.

There often remains much unfinished business in families where, for instance, a living person is not able to let go either. It is understood by ancient people that up to fifty percent of physical and mental illnesses are associated with "spirit attachment." "Family attachment" is not the only form of spirit attachment, for there is another sort associated with people who die not having gained any spiritual perspective whilst alive or, having indulged in alcohol or drugs, look to attach themselves to like-minded people. This makes an added difficulty for living people who are dealing with alcohol and/or drug problems. A third sort of spirit attachment occurs when a past personality from a former life reawakens in the current life. This situation can occur in the womb, and comes over at birth. This is maybe the most complex of situations and in extreme circumstances is probably associated with people diagnosed with schizophrenia and multiple personality disorders. This last sort of spirit attachment, when it is released, can leave a person for the first time to discover who they really are, and this is a time when that person can need a lot of support. It has been said that the whole of mental health needs to be re-assessed. The book by the psychiatrist, Sakuntala Modi, *"Remarkable Healings"*, makes very interesting reading. Also *"Freeing the Captives"* by Louise Ireland-Frey, MD.

Spirit attachment often comes as a surprise to many clients as the possible reason for low energy. It is common to find that the endocrine glands have no vibrating energy at all in this situation, for the entities live off the energy of the living person! In the long run, it is impossible for a person to benefit from any other form of therapy until the release of this attachment.

It can be especially difficult to explain to a mother that her four year old daughter, who died six years ago, is still with her and not able to move on to her next stage of evolvement. I have had to explain that this is not a good situation and together we have talked about the possibility that her daughter had completed what she had come to Earth to do. Completion can take place in just a few weeks, or a few years; every person is different. We gradually managed to reach a stage where the mother, along with the rest of the family, was ready to say, 'Goodbye'. However, support is needed over a long period of time in these traumatic situations.

Because people do not understand why certain situations have happened, they will always feel someone is to blame. The hospital perhaps or, in the end, "God"!

I frequently have to deal with a lot of confusion about the God concept. For many people God is "a Being" and therefore responsible for their misfortune when in fact, as Joel S Goldsmith discusses in a book first published in 1971, "*The Mystical I*", God is not <u>a</u> Being but the consciousness level known as just "<u>Being</u>".

I often say to clients that nothing happens by chance in our world because it is governed by perfect natural laws. The so called "Chaos" theories are conducted by unseen hands from a higher perspective.

Another client with a spirit attachment issue was a young man who, during his father's lifetime, did not have a good relationship with him. According to a Medium the client had consulted, his father was close by and this, the client felt, was a way of resolving past problems. When I explained that this situation was causing his very low energy problem, his comments were, 'Well I've had enough of this then!'

Many clients are unaware that entities are very often passed over at consultations with clairvoyants and mediums and this can also happen as a result of visiting therapists on a regular basis. It is an unfortunate situation that unless therapists themselves are balanced in mind, body and spirit their energy fields can attract entities like bees to a honey pot. People who talk about "protecting" themselves do not understand that the only real protection is for the consciousness polarisation to rise to a higher vibration where more light emanates from the cells and so entities, being of a lower life form, will not attach themselves.

Alongside "spirit attachment" other things affecting the person can be imprints coming down through the ancestral bloodline for many generations; these imprints can generate health problems or even curses carried by the cellular memory. This is how a condition like cancer, which has been dealt with at the physical level, can reoccur, perhaps in a different place at a later stage, unless it is released from the <u>cellular memory</u>. I call all these past-life difficulties "baggage" and <u>everything</u> I have mentioned can be released through correct spiritual healing.

Often I "pick up" a deep need for love. This can be directly linked to infancy and even treatment at birth. We tend to put babies in cots and prams from birth onwards, denying them the closeness of the mother's body as happens in less sophisticated societies. In a book *"The Continuum Concept"* which I read back in my Playgroup days, Jean Liedloff describes how we can go through life suffering from this lack of "in arms" experience. Of course this can affect us to various degrees according to our individual personalities. Incidentally, Jean Liedloff mentions how meditation can address this situation as we look inwards towards our own Higher Selves rather than expecting too much in our relationships.

Things affecting people through the ancestral bloodline can be very complicated. There can be health issues or merely difficulties which go back many generations. It's not difficult to imagine that ancestral bloodline issues could even, in some circumstances, be associated with the very rare medical conditions we hear of from time to time.

People are often anxious to find out more about their personal case but I prefer to say, 'Why analyse the dirt? Get a broom and sweep it out!' This was one of Gururaj's favourite sayings!

A few years back I had a student meditator who had had three people in her close family die of cancer within ten weeks of each other. Orthodox medicine is aware of what they call hereditary situations but of course it does not know how spiritual healing can release this. It is a lovely thought, I explain to clients, that they may have come down into incarnation with the mission to heal their ancestral bloodline, for once an individual is healed it affects everyone else in their bloodline. And something I have discovered was how the offspring of a relationship can set this in motion through the non bloodline parent! It is like the wonderful mirroring of the terrestrial World Wide Web but in a very silent way.

Before going any further and in the unlikely case that there be any doubt in people's minds, clearing an ancestral blood line has absolutely no relation whatsoever with a certain person's obsession with keeping the purity of the race during the last world war. Everything that I am describing is happening on a highly evolved level and is acting for the greater good of all humanity.

I have been very interested in what could be termed as a group healing process that has been taking place over the past couple of years. Mardiana is a very successful therapist who contacted me initially for a personal health issue. Due to her innate insights she realized how helpful it might be to try and extend the benefit to all her family, and this is what has happened. Step by step I have talked to her husband, daughter and sons, family from overseas and finally a large number of the extended family. It has certainly brought the whole family into even deeper communication with each other, crossing age differences and respecting cultural differences. Of course it has not been without drama, crisis, and conflict at times. Unconsciously, we actually set up situations for our own growth! Mardiana became conscious of the value of meditation over this time and so, following on from the course of meditation, she is now poised for my teacher training in order to offer this to a number of her clients who may want to learn. Apart from offering a listening ear, my part in all this process, as it is with all my clients, is to try and keep everybody feeling physically and mentally well so they can cope with everything so much better.

As time goes by I am being presented with more and more complicated conditions that I find are associated with irregularities of the endocrine glands which don't seem to be understood by orthodox medicine at present. These can be associated with the pituitary gland causing havoc in the body since it is the leader of the band so to speak. As is discussed later there is also a connection with man made chemicals. Hormones secreted by these glands are chemical messengers. An analogy, taken from the book *"Our Stolen Future"*, is that it is like an architect designing a house but all the inside pipe work gets installed in the wrong place! I recently described this to a young client as a possible scenario if her pituitary gland was not functioning properly. Once healing corrects the situation it will take time for all the "inner pipe work" to start functioning correctly! This isn't easy for a 20 year old to deal with! In comparison orthodox medicine appears to be so incomplete and this situation is unlikely to change while it continues to pursue its present approach!

My preliminary exploration also reveals the vibrational rate of all the glands of the endocrine system which secrete hormones into the bloodstream and, when in balance, regulate the whole body. Once the initial "baggage" is released and healing given, the vibrational rate of the glands will rise and this leads to all the cells in the body working more efficiently. It is possible to do this at a distance, anywhere in the world, and is just as effective as any "hands on" technique. When this has taken place any supportive nutritional supplements can be assimilated better. Again it is possible to determine the exact supplement needed, how much and for how long. It is completely unnecessary to be on supplements for evermore. The quality is also very important and I am able to "pick up" the life-force in any product. No life-force – which is very common especially for products sold on the High Street – means no value to anyone!

Renewal of the body now begins and it is an ongoing process. This is why I do a follow-up check and inform everybody if a need arises. This is a very valuable part of the work I do for I am beginning to see patterns that contradict many standard nutritional approaches in that I see that the body seems to prioritise its needs, seldom needing more than one, at the most two, supplements at any one time. Taking too many at a time is like mixing drinks! The body best seems to handle one thing at a time and this seems reasonable! I will come back to this subject in a later chapter...

The healing process is more difficult when clients, often the elderly, are on many orthodox drugs – especially those that are taken for blood pressure or thyroid issues. Following healing, the body is brought back into an integrated state and the cells begin to work better. Because of this, previous medication would need to be reviewed by the G.P. who prescribed it in the first place. However, it is my experience that, because the medical profession seldom understands the process of healing, it is reluctant to carry out this procedure, particularly in the case of elderly people. This can result in a situation in which medication actually works against the healing process. On this subject many of my clients do have to begin to take some personal responsibility for their health issues. I can only make suggestions and discuss ways of reducing drug dependence. I have nevertheless noticed that the healing process is definitely interfered with when clients continue to carry on with medication as prescribed before healing.

The body is able to heal itself if we trust this process. By doing checks and keeping everyone informed we can see some resemblance to the ongoing maintenance of a car, and human beings are infinitely more complicated than cars! However we also need this attention because, as I have already mentioned, we are changing as a species and this is consequently affecting our cells. In a book lent to me recently it indicates that keeping the endocrine glands in balance will provide the needed stability as more and more D.N.A. strands become active. I will also come back to this later.

Some interesting patterns are emerging on the subject of nutritional needs. Since I have developed my own graph for reading the vibrational rate of all the separate glands I have noticed that for the majority of people the thyroid and parathyroid usually give the same reading whether it be high or low. For a few clients there have been differences and where there are differences it has indicated a Ph acid/alkaline reading that moves towards acid. Now, the acid/alkaline balance is very important for it is associated with the oxygen levels in the body. It has been known for some time that low levels of oxygen always result in ill health. We know that oxygen is often given to people in hospital for all sorts of reasons although the oxygen given in these circumstances is nowhere as good as oxygen giving natural supplements. However, to go back to the clients with a thyroid/parathyroid discrepancy, the one supplement usually needed by them is Potassium which is an important mineral for acid/alkaline balance. It is an alkalinizer. Two people I was asked to look at had this thyroid/parathyroid imbalance. However they were not my clients but under psychiatric care, and no doubt this kind of approach would never enter the heads of the professionals who were treating them. However I have noticed that whatever I pick up as being needed corrects the imbalance in the glandular system and the client definitely feels better until a few months further down the line when something else will cause a change and I have to go through the whole process again.

More and more I am picking up the need for obscure minerals. Those that many nutritionists would not have heard of. On the other hand never do I pick up the need for a multi-mineral/vitamin supplement in the case of adults. Although a lot of knowledge is not yet available it is possible they cancel out benefits when put together. Some very important regenerative supplements are available but unfortunately, because people haven't reached a high enough level of consciousness as yet, they are unable to determine precisely what deficiencies they have and therefore what supplement might be of help to them.

There are many reasons why people may be lacking certain nutrients. One of them is directly related to basic food quality. For years the soil on which crops are grown has been deteriorating, leaving soil deficiencies and artificial fertilizers that can do more harm than good. This is, of course, one of the direct results of intensive farming methods which began after the Second World War. Practically every person I look at has a nutrient deficiency and since the body and mind are so closely linked this will consequently affect the mind.

After helping a client recently with a nutritional supplement, she said it was the first time she had ever felt really well!

I am beginning to be convinced that ill-health will continue to be misunderstood until we start to recognise the huge part nutritional deficiencies play in our health problems. Bio-chemists tell us that 90 nutrients daily are needed to maintain our bodies in good health although, on the other hand, bombarding them with dozens of unnecessary supplements can do more harm than good. If the drug companies are making huge profits then the supplement industry is not far behind these days!

Natural Progesterone is something I pick up a lot, for women at menopause time. Not every woman needs it but many do. A deficiency can lead to bad states of depression. What is much less widely known is how a lack of progesterone can also be associated with postnatal depression. Following childbirth it can easily happen that the oestrogen/progesterone balance does not return to normal. A while ago a woman was referred to me who had experienced "baby blues" after the birth of her third child. When anti-depressants from her G.P hadn't helped he had suggested she see a psychiatrist ... but in fact she simply needed progesterone.

As my study work continues I have become very interested in the part food allergies and intolerances play in our health, thanks to the naturopath, Peter D'Adamo, and his book *"The Eat Right Diet"* for different blood groups. He offers us the results of forty years' research, carrying on from his father's work, into the connection between diet and our blood group. I always take this book alongside Deepak Chopra's *"Ageless Body and Timeless Mind"* to any talks I give on health. Healing can always alter things a bit but what is vital information is the difference between allergies and food intolerances. The latter can often be addressed in the healing process but up to now allergies have seemed to be fixed. They can go completely undetected as was the case for myself until 1999 when a kinesiology test revealed a wheat allergy. Allergies could be completely unrecognised as playing a huge part in serious conditions of the digestion and bowels. They seriously impact on the immune system in a silent and sinister way exacerbated by our modern eating and cooking methods. It is most likely that we will ultimately adjust as we always have done throughout our evolution but in the meantime understanding the part enzymes play in the digestive process alongside the detection of various foods which are poisonous to our bloodstream can alleviate some very distressing conditions that are affecting young and old alike. I have started to systematically carry out an allergy test on all my clients after a few people, who had contacted me with digestive and bowel problems, brought this issue to my attention. In fact, I have very recently discovered that I can actually release allergies.

Due to their nature and the silent way they can affect people, it is pretty certain that allergies are associated with conditions that can get ever more complicated with age. It's amazing that standard allergy tests don't seem to be available in hospitals.

Last summer I had a young woman in her 20s contact me as her last hope to avoid surgery for the debilitating condition of Crohn's disease which involves inflammation and ulceration of the small intestine. This was diagnosed when she was 14 and up to the moment when she contacted me she had never had an allergy test suggested to her. She did have a wheat allergy. Following healing for clearing "baggage" coming down in both her parents' bloodlines, she started a supplement derived from silkworms, followed by specific enzyme tablets, and finally a powerful Co-Enzyme Q10. Her hormone system has now been balanced for the last four months.

After initial exploration I inform my clients of the situation and make appropriate suggestions. Although some cases need to be followed more frequently, I will do a recheck for all my ongoing clients and I contact them if any specific need arises.

At some stage of the healing process colour therapy or homeopathy may be required.

Where colour therapy is concerned it is very interesting to notice that certain colours are particularly called for. Orange, for instance, that recharges the subtle body and is an antidepressant. Magenta which is about "letting go" and is associated with fine chemical changes going on in the cells of the body. Indigo is a great healer and purifier. Green also comes up quite frequently. Being nature's colour, as one might imagine this is associated with emotional balance and harmony.

Recently I looked at a five year old little boy who was very often upset by tummy ache. I discovered that he had a wheat allergy but despite a wheat-free diet he still complained that his tummy ached. Talking further with his mother she told me that the separation with her husband seemed to be affecting her son's behaviour and that he missed his father. He needed green colour therapy to help his anxiety.

Homeopathy needed at this stage can often be at very high potencies. By working through names and although I am not a homeopath, I can determine the potency, the dosage and for how long it is required.

An interesting example happened the other day. A client mentioned to me that her five year old son was unwell. I checked and he needed homeopathy. This little boy had never had orthodox medicine so his mother was very familiar with homeopathic remedies but on this occasion, and although I have the names of over 300 familiar ones, none of these were indicated. His mother used the remedy-finder on the Internet and I kept checking but nothing presented itself and she was left to pursue the Internet further for as mentioned there are over 3,500 remedies! As I went to bed I asked my Spiritual Master for help in tracking it down! Early next morning the mother was on the phone – some remedy which had been used before, an unusual one, just jumped into her head - it would have to happen this way – and yes this was what little Stanley needed! I immediately did divining for the potency and guess what? His mother actually had one of the exact tablets needed to give him straight away! Thank you Gururaj!

As I say to all my meditation students; never anticipate the way help comes once we attain a harmonious state.

Patterns observed during the healing process suggest how the association between the physical and subtle body is very close. Interaction is constantly taking place. Humanity is certainly on the move!

Again, I'm often testing to see the effect of personal care products on people. If someone contacts me for a scalp problem the first thing that comes to mind is the shampoo the client is using. Health is a holistic approach and very much an individual thing. Recently a mother approached me for her eight year old son who had suffered from asthma, hay fever and eczema since birth. Along with his younger sister they are "Indigo" children which I will return to later on. All of these children have curiously needed orange colour healing at some stage.

Having tested that the personal care products being used in Oliver's family were certainly not doing him any good, I found two companies selling non-toxic, safe products and one of them was selling organic products. Although the family started using these products Oliver's symptoms didn't completely disappear. Eventually by a process of elimination I found that the culprit appeared to be the natural organic lavender, of all things… so there we are!

One must definitely not overlook the part that many other supportive therapists can play on the healing journey, for once the inner issues are addressed the internal energy system needs to awaken and begin to flow through the body again. As we know there are countless therapies to choose from. I have a list of over 40 or more that I can look at for clients at various stages. However there are some that seem to come up regularly and be very supportive for my clients. Therapeutic massage, Shiatsu, Cranio-Sacral Therapy, to name one or two, but there also others that may be helpful in individual circumstances, like Acupuncture or even doing Tai Chi. Where all therapies are concerned I always look to see how spiritually integrated the therapists are themselves. It is unfortunate that very few therapists seem to understand the true meaning of this at present. Celebrated names are no guarantee either! Perhaps, as consciousness generally rises, it will be increasingly possible to work more closely with other therapists which would certainly be in the best interest of all concerned. I myself now realise that I stayed far too long with my homeopathist who, whilst doing so much for me initially, did not "pick up" the necessity to address the physical body as well as other levels.

I am often asked about helping a person without their knowledge. It is, of course, very understandable that people want to help those they care about but nevertheless in most circumstances I explain that where adults are concerned their free will must be respected. The only exceptions are when a person is too ill to be consulted, with children and of course in the case of animals. However, apart from animals, I always ask permission from the Higher Self of an ailing adult or child. This might sound rather unnecessary where children are concerned but one must take into account the fact that in the body of a child there could very possibly be a highly evolved soul and health issues may even be part of evolvement for that particular individual. This may also be the case for a sick adult.

People often ask what part they might play to help themselves or loved ones during the healing process. I reply that because of our conditioning we are not yet familiar enough with the Higher laws of the Universe and that Divinity always responds when help is asked for. However "free-will" is one of the laws of our universe and even the Creator will not intervene unless "invited" to! I will come back to this further on.

This reminds me of a lovely story of a little girl who lived in one of the desert areas of the world. For her birthday she told people around her she was going to ask God for some snow. When it didn't happen they said, 'There you are, you weren't heard!'

'Oh yes,' she said, 'he did reply but the answer was No!'

Chapter 8

"The whole man is challenged and enters the fray with his total reality. Only then can he become whole."

Carl Jung

The journey through the door from fragmentation cannot really begin until the excess "baggage," due to spirit attachment and past life difficulties, is released through real healing. When this has been successfully accomplished, change of one sort or another is inevitably experienced through mental and/or emotional challenges. This can be a source of anxiety for many people and yet change is in the order of all things in life. We only have to observe the seasonal round of spring, summer, autumn and winter to rapidly come to realize that the whole universe is on the move. It is said "change is not the problem but our resistance to it". People generally have a fear of the unknown and it is precisely this apprehension that can cause trouble. Growth is evidence of life and always implies change.

We are living at a period in time when there seems to be an ever increasing push to evolve and move beyond aeons and aeons of re-cycling of our ancestors as they re-incarnate over and over again due to unfinished business and unfinished business is the making of the same mistakes over and over again.

I often say to people nowadays, 'Have a good think about that difficulty you are faced with and try to respond in a <u>different way</u>.' For until we manage to do this the same situation will keep being presented in similar ways. There is a saying "If you do what you've always done you'll get what you've always got".

Of course, if we are honest, we all have to face up to personal difficulties as we journey through life. The list is long but I would like to highlight some of the issues that could concern all of us at some point.

For instance difficulties surrounding "need" in a relationship. There is a trilogy of books *"Conversations with God"* by Neale Donald Walsch that got excellent critiques, has been translated into 24 languages and has now been read by millions. They are stocked in any good bookshop and most libraries have them or can get them in. From the question and answer style format it is said: "... but we all like to feel needed. Then stop it. Like to feel unneeded instead – for the greatest gift you can give someone is the strength and the power not to need you, need you for nothing." My Spiritual Master said, 'Devotion should be without need – it is the expression of love.'

Another issue that Gururaj also talked about concerns finding fault. "We very often consider that it is the fault of other people when the problem, in fact, resides in us... we project our imperfections upon others because we cannot handle them in ourselves. It would be so much more beneficial to recognize our own flaws that are mirrored in others and therefore try to improve ourselves. Unfortunately this is not usually what happens!"

On the subject of marriage or partnership, he considered that so many joint ventures are contracted or approached from a superficial level. "If a relationship is not raised onto a spiritual level then it remains on a superficial level which is rarely a satisfactory situation." In this as in so many other issues the foundation of meditation can gradually bring us to a different level of understanding where we learn that "all unhappiness is produced by our worthless sense of attachment". To be able to love without attachment is one of the greatest achievements a human being can attain. "There is no adversity in life, only opportunity." And to quote again from *"Conversations with God"* – "Let each person in relationships worry not about the other but only, only, only about SELF" – meaning the Higher Self of course!

The real meaning of positive and negative has to be grasped. Certain religions have completely misinterpreted things. Duality is given to us to learn through contrast; both the positive and negative charge gives us light! Everything around us is for our learning – left, right, up, down, night, day and, of course, male and female. We only have to ponder the two symbols of the ying and yang inextricably intertwined, the one highlighting the other ...

Fear in every form is what is holding us human beings back and creating the energy field that draws towards us what we fear the most! By being aware of this simple law of attraction I advise all my clients and meditation students to steer clear of any media sources that pull us down. It is always preferable to read and watch what is uplifting in life, to walk away from those people and places that do not make us feel good and to seek the company of those who lift us spiritually.

On the subject of "fear" from the *"Master Reflects"*, Gururaj says: "fear only comes from reflections and from memory". Projecting the past, the present is forgotten and we fear the future, "What is going to happen to me?" When we are living in the present moment we are fearless. Only memories create apprehension. So, how do we live without fear? There is only one answer and that is to reach the quiet of the inner mind. The force of the superconscious level then engulfs all the smaller, grosser workings of the mind. This is yet another reminder that the practice of meditation deals with all troublesome "thought forms" which is beneficial for the individual person and for humanity in general because every thought, good or bad, affects our environment. The more powerful the thinker the vaster the range of thought. That is why an enlightened person can affect someone twenty thousand miles away. This is how healing works and how questions are answered. Most people do not realize the power of thought – the silent impact. Negative thought can, on the contrary, be devastating much like termites that beaver away unseen and unknown until the house collapses. It is said "we all need to become visionaries or man will perish". All dis-ease is a consequence of negative thought and fear.

People very often completely underestimate the extent to which the mind can affect the body. Unhappiness and trauma, especially in personal relationships, can drain the body of its essential nutrients which in turn starves the cells of oxygen. This lack of oxygen in our cells is a major cause of ill health, for it upsets the delicate

Ph balance of acid and alkaline. Too much emphasis is now given to what is called "personal development" at the expense of misunderstanding the needs of the physical body, our essential vehicle throughout life. Having the gift of being able to read the health state of people's bodies I am observing the development of chronic ill health, a situation which is completely unnecessary from my perspective. All the talk about living longer gives a false impression for unless we can improve the quality of our lives, longevity could become a greater and greater burden both for ourselves and those around us.

According to the teachings of my Spiritual Master all the troubles of the world are the result of lack of integration. Fragmented people see in a fragmented way. Until we can recognise what this really means for us, we cannot ever expect to be free of illness, ailments and disease - dis-ease! Integration is the bringing into harmony of these three aspects of ourselves; our mind, body and spirit. We do not really need to spend hundreds of pounds attending "development" courses here, there and everywhere; often run by people who have not yet obtained integration within themselves!

How do I know whether a person has an integrated awareness of themselves? I can quickly pick this up using the same procedure that I use for every other question, be it about people, places, books, products, or even, for example, the vibrational rate of music. How different the world could be if we all had this understanding. However, if we don't yet have a specific gift we can be assured that life itself presents to us all the opportunities we need for growth – be it on a personal level, in the family or at work.

Two books I have found very useful are *"Why me, Why this, Why now"*, a 1995 book by Robin Norwood which teaches us to recognise the soul's purpose behind our encounters with adversity. Also Byron Katie's *"Loving What Is"*, where she presents us with "four questions that can change your life". Her other theme is that there are three sets of business – my business, your business and God's business – many people are rather too much involved in other people's business at the expense of their own!

It is not very difficult to notice the continual activity that surrounds us from morning until night. Mobile phones have increased this, for people can be contacted anywhere, anytime. There is no peace, no stillness. What are we trying to block out? There is not a lot of opportunity to reach that all-knowing part of ourselves, our Higher Self/True Self/God/Infinite Spirit. Eckhart Tolle, in his best seller *"The Power of Now"*, says "unless human beings can find a way of switching off from this constant chatter we will all eventually go mad!"

Perhaps we should also question the rush to the gym night after night or the running up and down the roads or even the dashing around on bicycles. What are we trying to achieve? Yes, of course, it is a good idea to do some sensible exercise but do we believe that this alone will keep us healthy? It is a bit like servicing a car and washing it down on a regular basis - unless there is fuel in the tank it will not move an inch! Do you know the French word for petrol? It is "essence"! Everything in creation works from the <u>inside</u> towards the outside.

Modern technology crams our minds from the start of the day to the end with, on top of everything else, the TV constantly on in the background in many homes. From his 1988 book *"The World is Sound"*, the writer Joachim-Ernst Berendt considers the move from radio to TV as being a step backwards. He says:

> *"for the person who gives priority to the ears amongst the senses, who is primarily a hearing, listening individual, this person we may logically conclude will be much less aggressive than someone who perceives the world primarily and initially through the eyes. For this reason the modern TV culture is a breeding ground for aggressiveness."*

Another great meditation teacher, Bhagwan Shree Rajneesh, has said:

> *"Eighty percent of your energy is devoted to the eyes. The other senses suffer very much because there is only twenty percent left for them. The eyes have become an Adolf Hitler. You have lost the democracy of your senses. Do not get too interested in pictures; otherwise you will lose more and more the ability to perceive reality!"*

We have to come to terms with all of these issues if we are to make the leap in consciousness which will allow us to move on as a human species. Some of us are now getting glimpses of DNA and cellular changes. As a species we have not yet set foot on this new land so the only thing that we can expect is the unexpected!

Chapter 9

*"... You can't behave appropriately unless
you perceive correctly ..."*

"A course in Miracles" – Author unknown

It would be foolish to deny that darker aspects of life exist. What could be called the "unbalanced negative" often shows up on a very day to day basis.

A good example of this is the much neglected understanding of how hormone disrupting man-made chemicals are threatening our "fertility, intelligence and survival". This is happening through food, drugs, personal care products and all household cleaning materials. Ten years ago it was considered that about 100,000 of these chemicals have become part of our everyday lives without us ever questioning their safety. In the book *"Our Stolen Future"*, written in 1996 by two leading environmentalists with an award winning journalist, we are alerted to the changes that have been taking place in the animal and bird population with their consequently profound message for the human race. This was surprisingly brought to light by Rachel Carson in her book *"Silent Spring"*, written some forty years ago and much of what she talked about so many years ago is now being confirmed by laboratory research.

We may do well to ponder the old Native American Indian proverb: *"Treat the earth well: We do not inherit it from our ancestors, we borrow it from our children."*

Hormones are the natural chemical messengers in the body. But more and more man-made chemicals are interfering with the body's communication network. They may not be actually killing cells but they are wreaking havoc in all sorts of silent ways which are not immediately recognised. They pose a particular hazard before birth and in early life and can change the reproductive system, alter the nervous system and brain, and impair the immune system. Some animal studies indicate that they can increase vulnerability to hormone responsive cancers such as malignancies in the breast, prostate, ovary and uterus. Conventional toxicological and epidemiological approaches could be missing the point.

As part of the holistic approach to health and healing we cannot ignore the part that personal care products play – deodorants, shampoo and toothpaste. Again much that is sold over the counter and in supermarkets contains toxic substances. We need to be very aware that the words "natural" and "organic" do not necessarily mean that they are completely safe. Products might contain a small percentage of natural ingredients but the rest can be toxic fillers. This also applies to "organic" food. One needs to look at the label and see if the Soil Association's logo is on there or UK5. The Soil Association does not grant that status until many years have passed cleaning up the growing process.

On the other hand there is also much talk trying to persuade people that "organic" is a merchandising ploy. However, by divining the life-force of a product I know straightaway the difference between organic and non-organic. One sustains health and the other does not. It is certainly encouraging to see that more and more supermarkets have a wide range of organic products these days. I have even seen up to 2,000 quoted!

Where toxic considerations are involved in personal care products, Samuel Epstein, M.D., Emeritus Professor of Occupational and Environmental Medicine at the University of Illinois and of the School of Public Health at Chicago and Chairman of the Cancer Prevention Coalition has written a book with Kim Erickson called *"Drop Dead Gorgeous"*. They warn of the hidden dangers of cosmetics which build up over years of use. Epstein has published some 260 articles and written books on this subject, *"The Politics of Cancer Revisited"* in 1998, and *"Genetically Engineered Milk"* and *"The Monsanto Milk Wars Handbook"* in 2001.

As far as orthodox medicine is concerned Dr Vernon Coleman, in his book *"How to Stop Your Doctor Killing You"*, points out that the person most likely to kill you is not a burglar, a mugger, a deranged relative or a drunken driver but, your doctor! Dr Coleman lists the medical profession as being one of the big three killers alongside Cancer and Heart Disease! He affirms that one in six patients is currently in hospital because they have been made ill by a doctor and that two out of five patients who are given a prescribed drug will suffer uncomfortable side effects.

Sherry Rogers M.D., an American doctor with 35 years' experience, has also written a number of books. Two of these are available in England – *"Detoxify or Die"* and *"The High Blood Pressure Hoax!"* published in 2005. She details how Western medicine in general and the pharmaceutical industry in particular (both of which focus on the masking of symptoms with drugs) actually make "the sick get sicker quicker and quicker". She considers that treatment with drugs is now the number one cause of death.

Information from the 1999 book *"Healing Codes for the Biological Apocalypse"*, by Dr. Leonard G. Horowitz and Dr. Joseph S. Puelo, suggests that electromagnetic technologies are having toxic effects and causing a spectrum of neuro-endocrine and immune system related disorders which can also be linked to reactions associated with eating grain products produced by modern farming methods.

And of course it is very important to talk of certain aspects of vaccination that feature a lot where young children are concerned and that are none the less relevant for adults. In a radio programme on this subject in 2000, Dr. Vera Shiedner spoke out very strongly against vaccination. She feels it is draining nutrients from the body, damaging the immune system and making the whole system more vulnerable.

Scan systems upset the endocrine system too; this I have picked up myself. It could be that the very systems devised to be preventive devices are actually as harmful as the reasons for them in the first place!

The American, Hank Wesselman, PhD, in a 2001 book, places his scenario 5,000 years into the future at a new primitive beginning where he meets his descendants trying to figure out why our world collapsed. He discovers that we fell from grace through our pre-occupations with gods of materialism, money, power, sex and status...

This darker aspect of many situations is perhaps given to us to help us to recognise things for what they are in reality in order to make choices for ourselves. Are all these common products and techniques helpful or destructive? Adequate reading matter exists everywhere and also, nowadays, on the Internet. We need to take sensible personal responsibility, for we are so often too quick to blame others for mishaps that might have been avoidable had we taken the time to inform ourselves and the courage to apply it! Knowledge, it is said, is power. In most cases health is a matter of choice. In the C.A.B., when I worked there, we often quoted to people "Caveat Emptor" or "Customers Beware!"

Interlude

Towards
the Unicorn

Ch'ilin
Ky-lin
Gazing out from
A world made transparent
By your exquisite beauty of form
Symbolism in your union of
Yin and Yang
Unknowable yet known
Creature in darkness of moon and
Lightness of sun
Purity through inner monastic existence
Cloven of hoof
Roughness of mane
Wisdom from horn of inner eye
You reign supreme forever
Powerful and free
Silently leading us into the
Dawning Age of Aquarius

Iris Sparkes

(Ch'ilin, Ky-lin – ancient Chinese names)

Chapter 10

"... Reality resides not in the external form of things but in their inner-most essence. This fact entails the impossibility to express anything real while lingering on the surface of things."

Brancusi - Sculptor 1876 – 1957

Perhaps at this point we might want to explore more deeply into the reason for our human existence on Earth, the impulse that started everything off.

Over time many Spiritual Teachers have talked about this. However the teaching from Gururaj's book *"The Path of Unfoldment"* brings a modern understanding and can enable us to see in more depth the ways in which we can work <u>with</u> the forces of nature to bring harmony and fulfilment into our lives.

One is rapidly confronted by the concept of a Creator and Creation. As I have already mentioned, it is important to move away from the image of "a being". If this is a source of difficulty, it may be help-ful to use a different terminology. Gururaj proposes Manifestor and Manifestation, thereby implying that it is in the inherent NATURE of things to BE this way, as it is in the inherent Nature of fire to give off heat.

Neale Donald Walsch in the latest of his *"Conversations with God"* books suggests that the word LIFE replace the word GOD. Looking at things in this light supposes that the Manifestor isn't separate from the whole manifestation of LIFE on Earth in all its different vibrat-ing energy forms and that can nowadays be observed under a power-ful microscope!

The process of evolution is inherent in every Soul as it passes in a natural way from the mineral to the plant and on to the animal world, during successive reincarnations, until it reaches the level of Man. At this point a major change takes place, as in becoming Man the Soul unfolds the ability to think.

This evolvement is, at the same time, a source of problems as the ability to think leads to the development of Ego, creating artificial boundaries between ourselves and the rest of the Universe. The principal desire of the ego is to preserve itself and an impression of separation develops, giving us a false sense of security. Having developed the capacity to think, Man can evolve as slowly or as quickly as he chooses, for he has discovered FREEWILL.

Due to this we have lost the natural instinctive knowingness of the former mineral, plant and animal stages. However, when we eventually re-discover all this and recognize our responsibility it will doubtless be on a far deeper level than formerly. We shall understand that nature acts and interacts in a PERFECT way to maintain equilibrium, which is one of the greatest laws of the universe. When we attain this stage we shall come to know that the Soul has played out its individual part in the Manifestation of the Universe.

However before reaching this awareness, "your primary duty is to recognize yourselves, to know yourselves. You are a God. You are an awareness and a consciousness. Everything is concealed in you. During this period mankind is becoming the first spark its Lord has created. This human being who will sit on the throne of consciousness, way beyond religions, will, one day, be the sovereign of the entire universe." (Quoted from *"The Knowledge Book"* accessible on the Internet.)

Alongside this innermost aspect of our Soul we also function with a Mind that operates via the brain. As the Soul is an individualised aspect of the Spiritual Manifestor, so the Mind is an aspect of the Universal Mind of the Manifestor. It is Divine, omnipresent and omniscient, forming the pattern of the whole universal structure into which everything is placed.

However, concerning this understanding and on a scale of time that is eternal, we could say that man is in a period of temporary difficulty. To use an analogy we have created the situation of putting ourselves into a sort of transparent plastic bag which contains water from the great sea of spirit but which cuts us off from the other parts of ourselves. All our thoughts and impressions, in vibratory form, from hundreds of lifetimes, build up around the plastic envelope forming many layers that obscure our perception of ourselves so we no longer know our source, the great sea of spirit WITHIN. This is sometimes called our "muddy pot".

The mind has three levels: the conscious ten percent, underneath which is the subconscious ten percent, and finally all the rest which is the superconscious aspect where pure thought originates. However, as pure thought comes through the "muddy pot", it reaches our conscious mind in a much distorted form. So, how do we start to clean up the "muddy pot" in order to untangle our everyday thinking, enabling our lives to become smoother and more pain free?

One way is, yet again, through correct meditation. This is perhaps the easiest way, for our ATTENTION is taken within, purifying the mind via a special Mantra, unique to us, which carries a powerful vibration that allows us to drift down to the superconscious level of the higher refined energy. This begins to affect the grosser levels of the "muddy pot", the subconscious. Meditation stills and quietens the activity there so we gradually become less affected by the babbling chatter of the subconscious. Over time, with regular practice, the "muddy pot" gets clearer and cleaner and more light from the superconscious is able to shine through, dispelling the gloom of troubled thoughts. Purer thoughts reach our conscious minds which raises the level of consciousness to a higher vibration rate. This, in turn, affects everyone around us and, like the ripples of a pond, extends outward to the whole universe.

Gururaj was often asked what the most important thing was that we could do to help the world and he always answered 'correct meditation' for until the overall level of consciousness is raised, nothing will change around us. Everything OUTSIDE of us in the world is reflecting back to us our troubled minds.

John came to learn meditation a number of years ago. He was on anti-depressants and had not worked for many years. By the end of the three month course of meditation he was able to come off the anti-depressants. Gradually he started becoming involved in self-help courses including counselling. At the same time he was also working through relationship difficulties and very traumatic childhood experiences. He had always felt that something had been blocking his development. He came to see me for a few healing sessions after which an opportunity came along for him to visit his home area which involved some powerful emotional reunions. Not long after this he attended the funeral of a relative who had been very close to him in childhood. This really brought things to the surface and for the first time he cried a lot. He rang me to share this quite profound turning point in his life for he said he felt Gururaj was saying to him "now you can start to get on with your life".

This doesn't mean John will necessarily sail off into calm waters for once "baggage" is released we can begin to deal with things that may have been put on the back burner!

This is a very moving story of how the "muddy pot" can start to get cleaned up while bearing in mind the personal effort we all have to make and the fact that it takes as long as is needed by the individual Soul.

We live in a very impatient world where everybody wants a magic wand to do things instantly! And yet, as I have already mentioned, we are living at a time when human beings may have an opportunity to move on as a species.

Chapter 11

"... Only after every conceivable emotion has been experienced, shall you know God ..."

"Earth's Birth Changes"
by St Germain through Azena

So, let's look again in more depth at the challenges that crop up all the time as the healing journey moves on.

Gururaj, who was always travelling around different parts of the world, spent many hours spontaneously answering questions and much of what is expressed here has been recorded by and is available through "The British Meditation Society".

RELATIONSHIPS are one of the forms of interaction that enable Soul growth to take place. Exploring further the nature of ATTACHMENT we notice an apparent paradox. For instance, two people can be totally devoted to each other and yet be non-attached. There is a difference between non-attachment and detachment. To take another example, people who are detached may exclude themselves from all on-going activities even to the point of becoming recluses. In non-attachment one is able to partake of any mind, body and spirit activity and yet be above all of it. Detachment can be a form of escape, the inability to face up to responsibilities. As the Bible says "Be in the world and yet not of it".

We have to look beyond the mundane to see deep enough to appreciate that nothing in this world is fundamentally ugly since it is a creation, a product of Divinity. Going beyond the surface value we can see the beauty within everything. Byron Katie writes "when we don't accept the actuality of any situation <u>we</u> are the ones to suffer..."

In her approach to counselling she observes that people think according to their patterned and conditioned minds, which obviously influences the outcome of therapy. This is far beyond the traditional style of help which, by not taking this into account, is very limited and can even make people more and more confused. Byron Katie, in her very special style, is achieving very rapid breakthroughs. A person's thinking pattern can change in a remarkable way to discover that every problem has its inbuilt solution. One can listen to her on CDs that are also available

Gururaj said that with acceptance comes surrender and we thus become free of "these impressions that cloud our perception".

One of the latest books in the *"Conversations with God"* series explores how spirituality in the future will be based on FREEDOM in relationships. People will choose to do whatever feels right for them, each person having the sovereignty of choice to accept things or not, for themselves, in a particular situation. Thus in relationship break-ups we can come to understand that we do not have any entitlement to possess another person.

Insecurity, another aspect of attachment, can be related to a lack of bonding with the mother at birth. And, as has already been pointed out, many people suffer from a "lack of arms" experience when they were infants. Thus, in later life, when relationships undergo strain, they can be thrown back to this stage which may also be exacerbated by past life issues.

Sandy first came to me for healing which included "spirit release". She had ancestral bloodline baggage and also current incarnation problems with her mother. After healing she went on to do meditation, an ideal follow on. For a number of months she had been trying to work at forming a new relationship which was causing some difficulties. Suddenly, in a public way, her partner threw things in her face which was obviously very traumatizing. This, she has had to discover, was perhaps a dramatic but probably deliberate way of bringing to the surface buried pain not addressed from the past.

To quote Eckhart Tolle in *"The Power of Now"*: "Relationships are not meant to make us happy but to give us opportunities to become more fully conscious ..." He reminds us that nobody hurts us. Pain is waiting to be uncovered so that our attention focuses on the problem which will thereby, hopefully, get resolved. Our buttons get pushed for very specific reasons at significant stages of our Soul evolvement. It is often said "everything happens for us, not to us".

SUFFERING is another area that needs exploring. Gururaj explained that it is the product of our Ego which is our human personality. This can lead us to discover that what we have always assumed to be real is not necessarily the case. Perhaps we may begin to question "Who am I?"

Humility develops when a certain issue is truly assimilated and we then gain control over it. It doesn't control us any longer. With greater SELF integration we gradually exude a strength that enables us to retain control. This understanding is the only way to go beyond suffering. Humanity is not made to suffer and even though the glass of the lamp is grimy true Light can still shine through.

Conflict in the mind creates illness because human beings are the greatest magnets in the world and we attract what we deserve. People do not realize that ALL fortune and misfortune is attracted to ourselves by ourselves. The Divine force within is the only force that can get rid of all our ills. There are books appearing now like *"Ask and it is Given"*, *"The Law of Attraction"* by Esther and Jerry Hicks, and Rhonda Byrne's book "The Secret" which has been made into a film and is available on DVD. All of these are bringing the subject to the attention of a much wider public. It literally means that whatever our attention is on will be drawn to us. So, on a lighter level, although we believe we are justified in paying attention to people who carve us up on the motorway, we ought to have another think because, by the universal law of attraction, more and more people are likely to do that to us!

If we acknowledge this then perhaps we can begin to understand how these greater laws of the universe operate. For example, the Law of "cause and effect", which is no other than the old saying already quoted, "as you sow, so shall you reap". All thought and action whether it be good or bad has appropriate consequences and all the different negative experiences, accumulated over millions of years, have to be resolved. However, by the Law of Grace, we don't necessarily have to relive each individual deed.

To illustrate this point my Spiritual Master talked of a sort of "credit balance". For example, someone who has done ten wrong deeds doesn't necessarily have to "pay" for them directly because if, on the other hand, he has done eleven good deeds he keeps his "credit in balance".

But perhaps one of the greatest gifts that Divinity has given us is the gift of forgetfulness. We all have an individual karma and at the same time we have a collective karma and as we improve ourselves, the whole of humanity improves too.

I constantly quote Gururaj who always said '... do not feel guilty about things you have done or caused to be done. You can go beyond your acts which can be discarded as one casts off a soiled garment ...'

One of the highest aspirations of each human being must be to try to harmonize the mind, body and spirit in order to find wholeness, for when these are no longer in conflict life assumes a different quality and this quality, in turn, produces happiness. The process and purpose of unifying ourselves makes us discover that Joy is the inherent nature of a human being.

Throughout the whole organic system, going right back to the primal cell, there have always been balancing factors. Everything in the universe is striving for balance but the thinking powers of human beings have upset this equilibrium, causing the illusion of separation which in turn causes illness.

Peter Erbe, in his book *"God I Am"*, discusses how to develop the tool of true perception. The laws of nature are always a help and support for us. Nature is never against Mankind since we <u>are</u> a product of nature. However, because we have the gift of free will, we often go against nature and that is when trouble begins!

Gururaj said '... the body is like a beautiful flute which is just a hollow reed, a piece of wood. We need to develop the attitude that it is "not <u>my</u> will but <u>Thy</u> will". Then the music that flows through the hollow reed becomes enjoyable not only to yourself but also to those around you ...'

This is the purpose of life but as the conscious mind is a <u>conditioned</u> mind we have to use a more subtle force in order to re-pattern and overcome conditioning. As greater integration takes place we become less dependent on external sources. This could be called INDEPENDENCE since the force power and energy that we use come from WITHIN and not from WITHOUT.

FEAR is a very big issue! Going back to what has been said about the law of attraction and how the mind attracts what its attention is on, we have seen how we draw <u>towards us</u> what we fear the most! Let's remind ourselves that we are not standing alone. Relativity walks hand in hand with the Absolute. "I am NOT ALONE ..." When we reach the quietude of the Higher Self we become saturated by that inner, higher vibration and fear has no place in that light. Fear is a superimposition upon us. To be fearless is to have faith in ONESELF. To have faith in ONESELF is to have faith in Divinity for the human being is Divine.

As this chapter draws to a close, let's muse on the famous HERE and NOW as it has been expressed by Gururaj "... if every moment is well lived then the next moment will take care of itself ... To enjoy each moment to its fullest is to enjoy the entirety of creation. Why should we remember that disobliging remark that was made to us yesterday? We are so accustomed to associating pain and pleasure. How pleasant it is to complain of being miserable! But as the stagnant water that lurks in the sponge can never be fresh we might conclude that if we wallow in misery we will end up smelling rather bad!"

Chapter 12

"... The Ocean separates not from the water.
The wind does not divorce from the air, neither
is the branch forgetful of the tree. Only man is
in ignorance of his Being which is God ..."

"God I am from Tragic to Magic."

Peter O. Erbe Australia 1991

So, how is sickness of mind and body related to all other aspects of life?

As we have seen we have had many relationships on our long journey through our different lifetimes and all the unresolved issues have come along with us creating various conflicts in our present life. This leads to the separation of mind, body and spirit and hence to illness, ailments and disease.

Many more people nowadays are beginning to question orthodox modern medicine, which is mainly based on the treatment of symptoms, because of the side effects of ever more powerful drugs. They are turning towards complementary, alternative approaches which explore causes. However, since so much is offered in this field, it can be very difficult to know where to begin.

Having the gift of being able to accurately read the vibrational rate of the glands of the endocrine system, I am able to see the effect that all approaches, whether they be orthodox or complementary, have on this vital system which regulates the whole body. Up to now this has maybe not been possible. It can challenge <u>all</u> present approaches.

As a result of my feedback, I can indicate a state of health, or illness, and I can also affirm that anything that doesn't raise the vibrational rate of these glands into a stable balanced state is not beneficial for this system.

For the same reasons it also appears that X-rays and scans can be a two-edged sword. The very things designed to check out a problem may immediately create another one for I watch how the glandular system is immediately affected with its vibrational rate often dropping to zero. At this point only correct healing will restore things. The glandular system is a sort of temperature gauge for the overall health of a person.

This was the case for a client who contacted me concerning a health issue. Following my usual procedure, healing first released family spirit attachment and an ancestral bloodline imprint that was impacting on her. A need for progesterone was then detected which is very common at the time of menopause. As I have already said not every woman needs it, but many do, for there is often an imbalance between oestrogen and progesterone at this stage of life. This is also a common hazard of modern times since there is so much mimicking of oestrogen in processed food and more generally in the environment. Anyway, my client, perhaps not properly understanding the situation, didn't try the progesterone cream but went to have orthodox tests and scans done. This caused her glandular system to be adversely affected. When she contacted me again, still feeling very unwell, healing was needed in order to raise the whole system to life once more and the need for progesterone was again indicated. However, since she is still on an orthodox drug she cannot expect to be restored to full health and we shall no doubt have to review the situation at some further stage!

Lyn contacted me following a mastectomy operation. After healing, which released the bloodline baggage impacting on her, I found she could benefit from a particular regenerative nutritional supplement which re-oxygenates all the cells. Her glandular system returned to a state of balance. However, as is often the case, she was persuaded to go ahead with standard chemotherapy and radiotherapy. This brought her glandular system tumbling down but after her treatment I found she could benefit from another amazing regenerative supplement. It is remarkable to see over and over again how our cells have such a will to live and resurrect themselves after serious disease and in spite of orthodox treatments which often have such devastating effects! Lyn also needed progesterone although this had to wait for her hospital treatment to finish. It then transpired that she had been given an on-going drug which is <u>not</u> compatible with progesterone. At this point Lyn had to decide for herself whether she trusted her body's ability to heal, or not. She has currently decided to see how see feels on gradually cutting down the drug for nothing can return to a balanced state until this happens.

Sadly, there are growing problems in the complementary health field with more and more people getting involved in all sorts of weird, so-called healing systems outside of the traditional therapies that have required a long training. Energies can be used in both a positive and a negative way according to the level of understanding and awareness. A lot of harm can be done with the best of intentions. There are no short cuts in the healing field. An invisible healing energy saturates the universe but before it can be beneficial to human beings it has to come through pure vessels. This involves purification that definitely cannot be obtained from a few weekend courses! It may take years of purification and certainly a lot of personal inner work to clean up the "muddy pot".

Unfortunately, up to now, with no real means of assessing whether a therapy or treatment is beneficial, both orthodox and complementary practitioners have been "working in the dark".

Prior to my current work as a "Health Intuitive" I spent a number of years observing the effects of colour therapy on people following my training in the 1990s. At that time I became mystified as to <u>why</u> I "picked up" that some people could <u>not</u> benefit from it. Gradually I extended these observations and realised that colour therapy can be an important therapy but only at a <u>certain</u> stage, for <u>some</u> people and at the <u>right</u> time.

I am sure that this is the case for other techniques and it would be to the advantage of all therapists to appreciate this. Of course many clients benefit from special care and attention which is often very valuable but if, as a species, we want to move beyond illness, ailments and disease, we will all have to gain a deeper understanding of ill-health in a holistic context.

Lizzie has been a client with me for over 18 months and when her hormone system suddenly dropped, following some distance colour healing, I knew something was wrong. On enquiry it turned out that she had innocently responded to a therapist looking for people to try his newly acquired skills on! She felt unwell shortly afterwards but didn't make the connection. Correct healing restored her hormone glandular system to its previous level and Lizzie will probably give more consideration to such propositions in the future!

As time goes on more and more people are crossing my path with what I have called "irregularities" in the glandular system. These are directly associated with ancestral bloodlines and linked in a karmic way. Once the imprints in the cellular memory are released, following healing, these irregularities are mostly corrected spontaneously. However, since they will have been present at birth, the whole system needs bringing into balance for the first time. This happens with the correct supplement or, sometimes, through colour healing.

It is very common for people to be taking thyroxin for what they consider to be thyroid problems. Of course this can be the case but, as I have already said, this gland is very closely associated with the parathyroid which raises blood calcium and maintains the calcium and phosphorus balance. Very few people mention the parathyroid which is surprising since problems here can give rise to bones softening. And in all the talk about osteoporosis we have heard a lot about calcium but very rarely about a possible link with the glandular system and yet unless the cause is addressed, whether it be by orthodox or complementary methods, symptoms will continue to manifest themselves.

The Pituitary gland, as I have already said, is known as the "leader of the band" and any functional irregularity here can lead to serious health conditions. In fact irregularities in any of the glands in the system are probably one of the major causes of ill health and have not been sufficiently taken into consideration by orthodox or even complementary therapists.

I had the especially upsetting case of three children in the same family facing the possibility of a risky operation because they had been diagnosed with a rare disease according to orthodox medicine. They had healing for a blood line imprint and their glandular systems were all brought back into balance. This is a typical example of possible discrepancies between what is happening at the deep level of the glands and what standard medical tests show on the surface.

I'd like to describe the interplay between the health of the body and lifestyle by describing the case of Ken. He first contacted me with what he thought was a problem of spirit attachment associated with drink and drugs. Following healing, he no longer felt comfortable drinking but he missed the company of his friends. It has taken a few years to restore his body via various supplements and I also encouraged him to take up some physical activity, feeling it would be supportive for him during this period. Due to an incident at work he had a massive electric shock which I believe was instrumental in provoking the powerful detoxifier that his body needed. It has not been a comfortable journey for Ken! A breakthrough for him occurred when, for the first time, we shifted attention from the physical to the subtle body via colour healing. As is always the case healing cannot proceed quicker than a person's Higher Self deems appropriate. Ken is gradually adjusting to a more balanced social life with everything in moderation and as time goes by he will probably attract company more suitable for his growing level of awareness. Being able to contact me has given him the ongoing support so necessary in such a lifestyle change.

Chapter 13

"... The most important thing is to live our present life at its highest possible level, spiritually speaking, to always place our search for its meaning before other goals. Then we must follow wherever our seeking star may lead us..."

"The Secret of the Creative Vacuum, Man and the Energy Dance."
John Davidson 1989

Healing that I offer people comes through me but not from me. Only Divinity knows what is needed for a particular Soul at a certain stage of its evolvement. Everyone has opportunities given to them and I believe that everybody who crosses my path is <u>ready</u> for a move on. It is so much more than a question of them "getting well and returning to business as usual".

I need to connect at a spiritual level in order to read the glandular system. In fact I can ask questions and get answers about <u>anything</u> concerning an individual. For example, whether they have any spirit attachment or imprints coming down their ancestral bloodlines, but only if they are <u>ready</u> to be helped can I look at the situation in their glandular system. This, I believe, is directly associated with Soul evolvement.

In the early days I wondered how I would respond if somebody asked for help and I couldn't connect with them. However, over all the time I have been doing healing work <u>never</u> has anyone rung me whom I couldn't help. Also, as previously mentioned, many people contact me on behalf of a relative or friend they would much like to help. However, unless the person in question is very unwell, or in the case of children or animals, I cannot do any work until they arrive at a stage where they feel ready to ask for help themselves.

Following healing I often explain that very profound changes may have occurred. This is especially so where ancestral bloodline imprints have been associated with irregularities in the glandular system. In this case things will never have been working properly since everything comes down via cellular memory. Every person in the bloodline will be carrying the same irregularities which can become complicated when one considers the mix between bloodline partnerships. Once again, I always say to people that they have perhaps come into incarnation to release their whole bloodline. Healing on one person will release "baggage" for all of the other people in the ancestry which means it will also correct the irregularities in the glands throughout their bloodline.

It may be the first time ever that this kind of "baggage release" can allow a human being to evolve. The majority of people have never experienced a fully functional glandular system and so one needs to be patient while the inside pipe works adjust to the new situation! Reactions are varied. Some do not initially notice any difference. Many comment on feeling tired which seems reasonable since we perhaps need to take things easy while adjustments are taking place. Of course, this will be temporary but temporary according to how long the body requires!

I'm beginning to find that sometimes specific physical therapy can be useful in enabling energy to begin to flow more easily through the body via the corrected glands. The two therapies that seem to be particularly helpful at this stage are Cranio-Sacral Therapy and Reflexology providing that the therapists do not offer anything else and on condition that they are integrated people because as I have said before, however well-intentioned they may be, any imbalances will be passed over. I always check this point for my clients.

Following release of entities most people experience a sudden lightness. A particular supplement will usually be required to re-nourish the physical body. In most cases this is an oxygen-giving supplement since entities live off the energy of their hosts because they are unable to detach themselves. They need help to be able to reach Light realms for higher healing. I always do a dual thing in these circumstances. I ask for release from the living person and that the entities themselves be taken to the Light. My understanding is that Beings of Light assist and I never need to interact personally with the entities although I know that some spirit release therapists do.

Probably the most changes occur when someone is living with one or two past-life entity situations which re-awaken to affect the person in this life. This is a subject which is not yet very well understood in the Western world. Before release of these kinds of entities some people may observe rapid changes of mood or personality. Unlike other "varieties" that can be opportunists looking for comfort, past-life entities, as their name suggests, have actually been part of someone's personality but in a former life. It is my perception that due to a previous traumatic life-time, former personality energy is awakened in this life.

One of my clients told me he was aware that in a former life he had been a black slave and had been pursued and killed. However the majority of my clients do not have any idea about their previous lives. It is very often when we talk about present relationship difficulties that the subject comes up. They describe situations where, in a matter of minutes, they have outbursts of totally unexpected emotions to the extent that they don't know who they are and people around them don't know either! When we get onto this subject, bells start to ring and the majority of clients usually want to tell me how this may have affected their lives!

After healing has taken place people need quite an adjustment to get to know themselves for the first time. Quite recently I had a man say to me, 'Well, I know I have a nice side and a grumpy side, but I do hope I am left with the nice side!' Another client with a dual personality problem where anger was coupled with a strong desire to control everything is now learning to see her husband do some of the day to day chores in his own, different, way. To use an analogy it is a situation not unlike a child learning to walk for the first time when they tend to be up and down until the new skill is mastered. Whatever the situation, I do like to encourage people to see it all as a new adventure.

Colour healing can be very helpful in dealing with ups and downs of the emotions following release. Suitable supplements can also help to ease stress and homeopathy at high potencies may also be indicated for past-life issues that are causing trouble in the present.

Whatever the case I pick up what seems to be the most appropriate in the situation, according to where each individual person is on the healing journey. However it is important to take time to explain possible changes. For example, supplements that were indicated before will probably change because they will be assimilated quicker since the cells will work at a higher rate. New supplements may only be needed for a short time. There is absolutely no need to be on supplements for evermore!

At this point it may be useful to say a little more about supplements. Of course their quality is obviously very important. One should always be very wary of offers such as "Two for the price of one!" In this field there is no secret. We get what we pay for!

However another important aspect is the length of time supplements should be taken for. Here again we are so used to the idea that a supplement should be on-going. This is really not so. When the body gets what it needs it is very often beneficial to give it a break from time to time. Many of my clients have to adjust to this idea, believing they always need something. For these people I usually suggest that instead they spend money on good organic food. If they were to develop a nutritional deficiency I would pick it up during my rechecks and let them know what precisely was required.

One thinks less often of how different substances interact and how they can, in certain cases, interfere with the healing process. Recently an 18-year old rang up to say that a particular supplement was making her feel sick. My first question was, 'Are you taking anything else?' Although she said 'No' we finally discovered that she was taking a hair growth product that had been recommended to her. After looking into this I discovered that the two were incompatible. It was not surprising she was feeling unwell. In fact she eventually proved to need a potent detoxifier to clean up the body!

A similar thing happened when I found a client was using an anti-wrinkle cream at the same time as a supplement.

In yet another case I had suggested a liver cleanser to a client who decided also to take another product that she was convinced would be beneficial to her. The media is often very persuasive to vulnerable people! Not long after, she rang saying she had come out in a rash. Once the whole situation was brought to light, I explained that the liver cleanser was probably doing a very good job getting rid of something that was obviously not right for her. Not long after, I wasn't surprised to pick up that she also needed a product that is indicated when there is a general clogging up of the body!

Another source of difficulty along the healing path is when a client's belief system prevents them from accepting a product, even if their lives depend on them taking it. I was confronted by this problem with the client suffering from Crohn's disease and who refused to take any animal derived products. I explained to her that her body seemed to need this product at that point and that it was just a temporary phase that she ought to try to accept otherwise the situation would deteriorate. This is unfortunately what happened and the result is that she now needs an oxygen regenerative product. Hopefully, following this, the next step will include something she can agree to take. It is nevertheless interesting to notice that the very supplement her body needed was one that was a challenge to her belief system. It shows how the innate level of consciousness is aware of what is good for the body without being obliged to take into account beliefs formed in the mind.

However, going back to the case of my client who refused a product, one might be tempted to think that it doesn't seem very important since she will no doubt be able to take something else later on. In other words, let's consider what happens if someone, for whatever reason, doesn't take what is indicated. I have often seen that in this situation, it is a bit like travelling down a main road and meeting an obstruction. Instead of clearing the obstruction (by taking the product) there will usually be side-roads and after making a detour we will be able to get back onto the main road. In this analogy the journey has been delayed and for the healing process it is the same thing. However the shortest road is not necessarily the best for everyone. Gururaj often said, 'Although I have a map that can show you how to get from London to

Southampton by the quickest route if you choose to go all up the East coast to Scotland and down the West coast in order to arrive on the South coast, that might be more evolutionary for you!'

And talking of evolution brings me to talk now of one of the most subtle aspects of the Healing process. Working as I do on a vibrational level, it is possible to get an indication of where someone is on their own evolutionary journey.

There are four levels that affect us. The Physical body, the Mind level with its mental and emotional challenges, the Etheric level with Soul issues and the Causal level which is our "blueprint" for this incarnation. The "blueprint" is the issues that we have come into this incarnation to address. To begin a healing process is to give people the opportunity to experience all of these levels. Patience is often needed to trust the healing powers of the Physical body. We are often confronted by the trials and tribulations of mental and emotional matters and yet the momentum of life propels human beings ever forward especially when baggage has been lifted. Many people have difficulty moving beyond this stage. However, specific colour healing can assist here and often gives indication as to the Soul matters that might be engaging a person. This is a period in which people are often brought to a different perspective on life. At the Causal level we will have accomplished what we set out to achieve in this life. As we move beyond this level what is awaiting us is DNA and cellular changes. The support of particular colours which are associated with these subtle energy levels can help to smooth our passage as we negotiate unexplored territory with trust.

Since the endocrine system is so closely associated with all the chakras perhaps we can better understand how the health of our physical body can never be treated without taking all the other levels into consideration.

Edward Bach, who discovered the famous Bach flower remedies many years ago, talked about the real cause of illness as being a separation in the unity of mind, body and spirit. He felt that this was initiated by the thought patterns of the mind and this is why he developed preparations designed to address the situation at an energetic level. This was, of course, very little understood at the time. These remedies can be very helpful at certain stages although the decision to suggest them, as with anything else, is always subsequent to my picking up a positive response for them. There is such a wide palette of helpful substances and techniques but everything depends on knowing what is useful and when.

As time has gone on I have seen what a huge part the correcting of irregularities throughout an ancestral bloodline plays. However, all the people involved are individual souls on their own unique path and the glandular systems of each will need something different. This is usually a nutrient but it can occasionally be colour healing. By looking at all my clients regularly, I am able to keep things in a balanced state. It can be months before people need to make contact again.

On the observational level, I nonetheless have the impression that vibrational changes are speeding up. Whereas before colour healing was wanted at a slower daylight speed, nowadays higher accelerated colour healing is very often needed. I will come back to this later on.

I have also discovered that I can give colour healing by using a person's name since every letter carries a specific vibration. Healing is therefore immediate and doesn't have to be put off until I actually receive a photo of the person. Maybe this is the right time to outgrow constriction and to re-create ourselves anew for we <u>can</u> be masters of our own destiny

Chapter 14

*"The important thing is to be able, at any moment,
to sacrifice what we are for what we could become."*

Anon

From all my checks, patterns are developing showing we may need to examine current approaches with some urgency. This particularly shows up in the field of nutrition.

Caroline came to me after a long search for the answers to the M.E. she has had for 12 years. She had a very impressive list of all the latest data feedback from a highly reputed nutritional establishment which suggested she needed no less than 15 supplements. I did an initial releasing of "baggage" involving spirit attachment and bloodline imprints in both her ancestral lines. I then examined the list of supplements she was taking. They were of good quality but not <u>one</u> of them was doing anything for her glandular system. We phased them all out and replaced them with just one supplement. That, coupled with natural body renewal, is quite sufficient to gradually address the balance of her endocrine glands <u>one</u> step at a time and according to how her body wants to prioritise.

This pattern is showing itself in all my work and suggests that things happen very differently to the way one might expect. It seems to indicate that the body itself has an inbuilt intelligence that goes beyond our present observation through outward tests. This could be indicating a lack of perception on behalf of the observer for I am sure that what the external tests show on <u>one</u> level is correct. However there seems to be general misunderstanding of how correct nutrition takes place.

For instance, if tests indicate the lack of one or more nutrients, it is of general practice to take them in the form of supplements in order to resolve the problem. This is a very understandable approach but from my observation this does <u>not</u> seem to work. So why is this? And what is the alternative?

I think that by identifying the one correct substance that the body needs at a particular moment it will then act as a catalyst for other nutrients to develop by themselves. Thanks to my gift of divining I am able to get feedback on this process at the vibrational level of the endocrine glands. This is probably vital knowledge necessary to further our understanding. However, I am aware that this is really not very welcome news for the supplement industry!

I am very often at variance with those who only use machines to obtain information about nutritional deficiencies. For obvious reasons mechanical measurements cannot assess a person on a holistic level. And yet, unfortunately, it is this fragmented approach which is prevalent in our modern perspective on health. In the Western world we have gained a lot of understanding but we are very far from considering people in their totality and other issues are appearing as a direct result. We must go beyond symptoms as they are definitely not the whole picture.

Joe is 14 and suffering from diabetes. Following a junior supplement necessary after healing, his glandular system did not come into balance as I had expected. This suggested that the insulin he was taking was interfering with the process. Joe's mother very courageously decided to try to reduce his insulin dependency very slowly, drip by drip. She is observing the following pattern. At each step his blood sugar shows a sharp rise. This stays for a few days and then it lowers. Alongside this I am keeping a check at the level of his glands. At various stages there have been fluctuations. He has needed indigo colour healing for purification and latterly yellow has been used to improve the vital flow through the body. At each stage balance has thus been restored. These colours indicate that subtle levels are involved. Naturally I am quite aware that for many people, including the medical profession, bells would be ringing and hands going up in horror at the very idea of trying to reduce insulin for a person with diabetes!

However, let's explore further in light of the understanding that our body <u>can</u> heal itself. When we cut a finger it heals up. Can this not be extended? I believe that the body has all the innate intelligence it needs to heal itself, provided we know how to help and support it. When we consider things from this point of view, what may look like a chaotic situation on the surface could be the body adjusting to the new situation and beginning to do things in its <u>own</u> way.

Another client contacted me for help following a standard test showing high levels of homocysteine in the blood. This is a situation often associated with the risk of heart attacks. Following healing she needed a tissue salt which brought her glandular system into balance. She felt well and was due to go abroad on holiday, in spite of a routine follow up test that still showed no change in the homocysteine level. I believe that what was showing up in the tests was <u>not</u> the whole story but rather an interim stage.

Of course much of this is a very new perspective and not everyone that crosses my path will trust the process. I was particularly sad to learn that a beloved dog was put to sleep, by decision of the owner and a homeopathic vet, because they could see no obvious change for the better in a bone tumour. After healing she needed just one tablet at the highest potency in homeopathy. After taking this I could see that the glandular system had come into balance and I do feel that her body probably just needed time to undertake changes at a surface level.

Everything in creation works from the <u>inside</u> to the outside. Because we cannot actually see what is happening inside, we have to gain a different level of awareness in order to apprehend things and thus to be able to appreciate the totality of a situation. This is probably our next leap in consciousness.

Another aspect of my work concerns the compatibility of drugs, nutrients or other substances when they are taken together. Because I often get clients coming to me who are taking orthodox drugs, part of the work I do is to see how compatible these are with any natural supplements that may be indicated. They are sometimes compatible to the extent that they are not <u>in</u>compatible. No drug ever registers as being good for the body which is understandable as it is all the same a "foreign agent". However this is also the case for some natural supplements. For instance a herbal preparation might not be correct for a certain person. The preparation may contain high quality herbal products but, again, so complex is our individual body chemistry that mixed with other substances incompatibility can occur.

Due to the way I can pick up positive or negative vibrations I have gained what could be considered as a new understanding on the issue of man made chemicals. In the same way that natural supplements can be compatible or incompatible due to their <u>mixing</u> together, the same may be surprisingly true of these chemicals. I would even go as far as to say that in some cases they may even be helpful at a certain stage of the healing process, when they are used with proper understanding.

This is something I have discovered recently as a result of the case of a client, Val.

She has had many health problems for about 12 years. Thanks to a herbalist, things were more or less under control, but there was no great improvement. A herbalist's training will, of course, involve product quality and yet, unexpectedly, she seems to need products that are not quite as pure as those recommended.

This sort of observation alongside others that I am making could be quite a challenge to many people, especially those who are working in specialist fields, but when one takes a look back in history, current thinking has often been turned upside down by new information. This has usually been accompanied by a jump in the level of consciousness and could be attributed to people favouring processes associated with the right hand side of the brain, as opposed to the logical, analytic processes of the left hand side.

Sometimes one does indeed discover things in such unexpected ways!

I woke up one morning with a toothache. This had not happened for many years. I made a dental appointment, was given an X-ray and told I would have to wait for a couple of weeks for another appointment. I had not taken any pain killer drugs for about 15 years but I was quite resigned to resorting to them if necessary. However, it then jumped into my mind to explore colour healing. Apparently I needed the colour purple although I couldn't see the connection between my usual understanding of this colour and my toothache! I looked up information from my colour therapy training and discovered that purple is an analgesic!

I gave myself the three or four sessions indicated through my divining and the pain gradually subsided. At first I thought that the colour therapy had acted as an alternative to a pain killer as by the end of the two weeks no pain had come back. When I rang to cancel the dental appointment, I was told that the X-ray had revealed an abscess! I replied that it seemed to have gone! I then realized that the colour therapy had done much more than expected and had apparently managed to treat an abscess! On a very down to earth level I appeared to have also saved myself a lot of money!

Following this, over the year, I had one or two gum boils but each time purple colour healing dealt with them.

In fact, thanks to my tooth ache I had also discovered something else which concerns the colour therapy technique. This was the first time I discovered that accelerated healing could be used as a pain killer but I will go into more detail about the accelerated colour healing technique a little further on.

Since this discovery a number of clients who have contacted me with the onset of pain have been successfully treated by accelerated purple colour healing. Nevertheless it would be denying a complex process to consider that colour healing can always replace a chemical drug. Some pain needs a different response. As already suggested the body will only address pain when other priorities have been dealt with.

An elderly client was complaining of pain in her joints when she first contacted me. However, in her case, many other things seem to have been more important to rebalance before I picked up the need for a supplement directly linked to the pain in her joints. As they say "Everything comes to those who wait!" In her case it was nearly a year!

There is no way the body will respond until it is ready. People are so used to having their symptoms relieved, which is quite understandable, but eventually there is a price to pay, for this attitude can lead to serious conditions.

On this subject, a little book by Louise L. Hay, *"Heal your Body"*, gives helpful insights into the possible mental causes for physical illness and the metaphysical way to overcome them. This is set out as

"Problem and possible Cause" and offers advice on how to create a "new thought pattern".

However, to return to the subject of colour healing, I do feel there is very probably so much more to learn about the power of colour in the healing process but, yet again, in the work I do things just seem to cross my path in unpredictable ways!

By chance, or rather I am sure it was not, I was away for a weekend in the summer. Since discovering the benefit of more accelerated healing I had given it from time to time as, for instance in the case of a client who crossed my path in a rather hysterical state. Accelerated colour healing involves the use of a light box which works with electricity rather than the slower, daylight method which, in general, had always seemed more appropriate before. Nevertheless, that summer, I had taken my colour light box with me in order to continue healing for a few clients but, lo and behold, as I plugged the box in, the little light bulb blew! How curious! Was this going to be significant? Had it happened at home I would have simply replaced it with an identical 15 watt bulb but, in the only nearby shop, they had every wattage except 15! I therefore had to experiment with a slightly stronger light bulb. This turned out to be not only a temporary substitution for that weekend but what one might call a real discovery, for I have started to use the stronger light especially in situations of pain.

I had obviously been given the opportunity to move further on. I am more and more convinced that everything is associated with how the body undertakes its own healing path according to an inner order of priority. When this is understood we can return to full health if we are prepared to be patient. Unfortunately this is not a quality that we see very much around us today!

From time to time one gets glimpses of amazing spontaneous healing episodes which reveal our potential as human beings. In *"The Aquarian Gospel of Jesus the Christ"* written by Levi we can read, "You know that all my life was one great drama for the sons of men. I lived to show the possibilities of man."

There are still many children who are born carrying ancestral imprints associated with the glandular irregularities that so often lead to health problems but I have also noticed that very different children are coming into the world. They are different to the extent that they are not carrying any baggage via the ancestral bloodline and they also appear to be closely linked together in that what <u>one</u> requires, when the glandular system becomes unbalanced, they <u>all</u> seem to require. I shall return to them in a later chapter.

Homeopathy is another form of healing that I often pick up. However, I have noticed that for me it is rarely a first response and that other stages have to be reached before it can be helpful. This is probably one of the reasons that explain why it seems to be needed at exceptionally high potencies.

A middle-aged man contacted me because he was having a lot of difficulty adjusting to a divorce after 25 years of marriage. Much support was needed, in different forms, but eventually it seemed that he could benefit from a homeopathic remedy associated with digestive problems. It was obvious that on a higher, symbolic level of understanding he was having difficulty digesting the changes in his life. He needed high potency homeopathy and when it is taken at this level I often find that just one tablet is enough to bring the glands into balance. In fact I can literally follow the rebalancing as the tablet dissolves in the mouth.

I have also noticed that animals respond very well to homeopathy and that, following healing, the higher potencies are very quickly effective.

Perhaps too, a very important role for homeopathy is emerging in that some homeopaths who have a machine are able to mimic drugs as a non toxic alternative and so help a person come off a drug where this is preventing the overall healing process.

Chapter 15

"Those who love wisdom must investigate many things."

Heraclitus

Healing can bring about very subtle changes which are not always recognised as being the direct result of the healing process. Changes operate in very personal ways according to how the individual can best handle things. The Karmic links which have bound us together are now also being released through the healing process, leading to changes in all kinds of relationships. Likewise family life as it has evolved over time to accommodate "unfinished business" is probably going to be transformed.

As Karmic links are released they are acting as though a line has been drawn under unfinished business, a settling of the accounts that is wiping the slate clean so that we can move on as human beings. Our consciousness polarization is moving upwards from the solar plexus where all the emotional baggage is stored, to the heart chakra where unconditional love resides. My Spiritual Master always said his own mission was to "open the human heart".

And didn't the Master, Jesus, say, 'For, if I be lifted up, I will lift all men'? He was, of course, meaning "I" to be the Christ consciousness in all of humanity.

The scientists who talk of "junk DNA" have a rather limited perception of the wholeness of life. Is it really possible for anything to be absolute "junk"? Of course it is not. Everything in creation is very meaningful, just waiting for us to find out more about it.

It is certainly fascinating to see how more and more DNA strands are becoming active. This could release greater healing ability. Peter Erbe, in his 1994 Australian publication *"God I Am"*, suggests that some of us are becoming "frequency modulators" thus altering the vibrational rate of others around us.

I have noticed that in some circumstances, when I connect very easily to a client just through thought alone, the healing process immediately begins and the vibrational rate of the endocrine glands is raised almost as if it were an automatic process.

Some months ago I was asked to see what might help a 20 year old young man diagnosed with Asperger's Syndrome. This is thought to be a variant form of autism but controversy exists amongst professionals as to the dangers of extending this label to all forms of difficult behaviour. However, completely outside of the debate between specialists, I have this gift of being able to pick up the cause and best treatment for any physical or mental condition. I can "tune in" which is a bit like hearing a musical instrument once it is played. So, I went through all my usual procedures and certainly picked up the vibrations suggesting an abnormality in the amygdala area of the brain which generates emotions from thoughts and perceptions. This is the area I feel is associated with difficulties in the lives of people considered to have Asperger's Syndrome.

However, some hours later I decided to do some re-checking on this young man and to my astonishment all the original vibrations had normalised and now all that was needed was a particular nutrient to complete the process.

Here I was confronted by what appeared to be spontaneous healing. I was a bit concerned about what seemed to be a return to a fully functional brain but believing, as I do, that nothing happens by chance I have to trust that all will be well for him eventually. Colour healing has been important as a follow up and changes have been observed but difficulties obviously still remain and much family implication and support will of course be needed.

Listening one day to a woman talking on the radio about her career as a profoundly deaf singer, unknown to many around her, I became very interested when she mentioned that deafness was in her family. As on previous occasions when I explored the situation I found imprints coming down through both her ancestral bloodlines. I felt that this could be the cause of an irregularity in the pituitary gland which, in her case, might be manifesting itself as deafness. As I continued to explore I suddenly noticed that everything seemed to have been corrected. I felt I had to write to her, via the radio programme, explaining that I had no idea what might be the outcome but that a little miracle had maybe taken place! She responded that she would follow up on the supplement I suggested for her and that she would keep in touch.

I have also noticed that when spontaneous healing takes place it is always in cases of people who are showing remarkable courage in overcoming their affliction.

I was given a recording of a TV programme that concerned a young man who was born with a debilitating condition called Cystic Fibrosis. This is characterised by chronic infection of the respiratory tract. He has an amazing musical talent and displays such a positive personality despite having to spend long periods in hospital. I was of course interested to look into the position of his endocrine glands and it wasn't surprising to discover that his pituitary gland was hardly functioning at all. As I carried out this observation I felt an unusual power was coming through the divining force of my pendulum and even as I was exploring, all the vibrational rates of his system changed and the pituitary gland was corrected. Once again healing appeared to have taken place in a spontaneous way! However this teenager is on dozens of drugs that have, of course, enabled him to obtain some quality of life although with such a condition his future is uncertain. I know what this young man now needs but the drug situation is not compatible.

The most perplexing of situations to date is where a ten month old baby was badly scalded. At first when I looked at her name I picked up nothing, but a few days later when I looked again everything was vibrating, not fully balanced but suggesting Indigo was required. Indigo colour is for deep healing. I heard later that the little girl had died. When a human being dies in traumatic circumstances it is unlikely to find that they go straight to the higher realms. However, perhaps the deep healing process that took place had been helpful for when I checked after hearing news of her death, I found she had gone to the light.

Very few people in death are able to reach the higher realms without help which is why so much spirit attachment occurs.

Recently, on exploring this further, immediately following the death of a few people who were known to me, I have picked up a need for pink colour healing associated with Divine Love and the Soul has gone straight to Higher Realms.

Over the past few years, part of my work has involved "asking" whether a person has reached the Light. When this hasn't happened and if there is "permission" from the Higher Self, I "ask" for the person in question to be assisted. "Permission" from the Higher Self can indicate that this is timely. It seems that most souls leaving this dimension can need an interim period to resolve conflict.

It may seem hard to believe but I am able to "pick up", via divining, the positive vibrations of my bloodline family who have "died".

In fact it is possible to "know" information about any person from the past. Out of interest I have looked at many names of artists, musicians and famous people from days gone by.

Perhaps a long time ago all these sorts of happenings might have been considered as being miraculous but nowadays we are working towards the perception that absolutely everything in the universe functions through natural laws. So, although various events may not be fully understood yet they nevertheless obey natural laws. At some point in the future we shall probably discover how closely connected all different dimensions really are.

Now, how is all this different understanding, acquired through my personal experience, to be reconciled by those who have been trained to respect knowledge and information gained through the analytical method associated with processes situated in the left side of the brain?

The thinking mind, said Gururaj, makes a good slave but a bad master. He was thus indicating that real KNOWING is beyond the thinking mind. This is something I have certainly become aware of. Pondering on his beliefs at the end of his life, Carl Jung, the famous psychologist, who took understanding to a deeper level than Freud, said, 'I don't believe

I know ...' We access this <u>inner</u> knowing, once again, during correct meditation practices that afford us insight not available by other means. However, as time goes by, all this is likely to be confirmed through the science of quantum physics which will probably explore the whole nature of consciousness, thus changing our present day understanding.

Until this time has come we have to be willing to open our minds to all the other possibilities concerning the nature of "Illness, Ailments and Disease", for otherwise we shall continue to "see through the glass darkly".

David Hawkins, who has developed *"The Institute for Advanced Spiritual Research"* in Arizona, discusses how necessary all the Spiritual Masters have been, for they alone have counterbalanced, at one point in time, the thinking patterns of a majority of people and pre-vented self-destruction. He uses a graph to indicate humanity's state of evolvement. On a scale going from 0 to 1,000 he places the Spiritual Masters at 1,000. Prior to 1986, he estimated that 85% of the world's population was below integrity level, that is to say 200 on his scale. A more recent study has indicated that this is now true for "only" 78% and that this consequent progress is due to a relatively small number of evolved human beings. As with all measurements based on averages, when considered individually, the large majority of human-ity is still below the level of integrity.

Of course, we need to replace this type of assessment in the whole context of David Hawkins' work but I am quoting it as yet another indi-cation that we are indeed heading upwards after aeons and aeons of evolvement.

Throughout history it has often been a single person who has chal-lenged current ideas. To take just one well known example, Galileo, the famous astronomer, was forced to deny his new understanding that the planets and the earth revolved around the sun.

It is still a matter of choice as to whether we can make this next leap in consciousness facing up to the necessary emotional and/or mental challenges as we walk through the door and begin the journey of real healing.

Perhaps we could also consider words spoken by one of our world's great statesmen:

"Our deepest fear is not that we are inadequate, our deepest fear is that we are powerful beyond measure. It is our light, not our darkness, that most frightens us. We ask ourselves 'who am I to be brilliant, gorgeous, talented, and fabulous?'

Actually, who are you not to be? You are a child of GOD. Your playing small doesn't serve the world. There's nothing enlightened about shrinking so that other people won't feel insecure around you. We are all meant to shine, as children do. We were born to make manifest the glory of God that is within us. It's not just in some of us, it's in everyone. And as we let our own light shine, we unconsciously give other people permission to do the same. As we are liberated from our own fear, our presence automatically liberates others."

Nelson Mandela

Interlude

My Law –
Tieme Ranapiri

*The sun may be clouded, yet even the sun
Will sweep on its course till the Cycle is run
And when into chaos the system is hurled
Again shall the Builder reshape a new world.*

*Your path may be clouded, uncertain your goal
Move on, for your orbit is fixed to your soul
And though it may lead into darkness of night
The torch of the Builder shall give it new light.*

*You were. You will be. Know this while you are
Your spirit has travelled both long and afar
It came from the Source, to the Source it returns
The spark that was lighted eternally burns.*

*It slept in a jewel. It leapt in a wave
It roamed in the forest. It rose from the grave
It took on strange garbs for long aeons of years
And now in the soul of yourself it appears.*

From body to body your spirit speeds on
It seeks a new form when the old one has gone
And the form that it finds is the fabric you wrought
On the loom of the mind from the fibre of thought.

As dew is drawn upwards, in rain to descend
Your thoughts drift away and in destiny blend
You cannot escape them, for petty or great
Or evil or noble, they fashion your fate;

Somewhere on some planet, sometime and somehow
Your life will reflect your thoughts of your Now
My Law is unerring, no blood can atone
The structure you built you will live in alone.

From cycle to cycle, through time and through space
Your lives with your longings will ever keep pace
And all that you ask for and all you desire
Must come at your bidding as flame from a fire.

Once list' to that Voice and all tumult is done
Your life is the life of the infinite one
In the hurrying race you are conscious of pause
With love for the purpose and love for the Cause.

You are your own Devil, you are your own God
You fashioned the paths your footsteps have trod
And no-one can save you from Error or Sin
Until you have hark'd to the Spirit within.

Attributed to a Maori

Chapter 16

"... Recognise what is before your eyes and what is hidden will be revealed to you ..."

The Gospel of Thomas

Over the years I've found it helpful to bring in certain aspects of a symbolic interpretation of the world around us because it can help us to understand the issues that we have to face up to and it is amazing how significant this can be in people's lives.

Esoteric numerology was part of my initial colour therapy training. It is based on the fact that every number and letter has its own particular vibration. Numbers can also be associated with a colour quality.

"Know Yourself Through Colour" is a book written by my colour tutor, Marie Louise Lacey. It was first published in 1989 and is worth searching for. We discover that the number 1 is about independence and leadership and that these qualities are associated with the colour RED. Number 2 is all about adaptability leading to harmony and is associated with ORANGE which itself is associated with the creativity and self expression that leads to confidence. Number 3 is associated with the pure artist, creativity and the colour YELLOW for intellect and ideas. Number 4 is about self discipline and practicality and is associated with GREEN, for energy balance and harmony. Number 5 is all about communication and is associated with the colour BLUE, for intuition and awareness. Number 6 is associated with responsibility and organisation, and the colour INDIGO is for power with knowledge and understanding. Number 7 is related to sensitivity and insight and the colour VIOLET is for high ideals, inspiration and intuition.

<u>Number 8</u> is linked to success in business affairs and the importance of finding the right balance between spirit and matter. It is associated with the colour SILVER, for unifying knowledge and awareness. <u>Number 9</u> is associated with service, benevolence, the giving of oneself with no thought of reward and the colour GOLDEN YELLOW.

Our lives go in nine yearly cycles and if the date of birth year is replaced by the current year it is possible to see where we are in this cycle.

Caroline, my client who has had M.E. for twelve years, was just coming out of year four of her life cycle when she contacted me. In the nine yearly cycle, year four is often difficult. It is in about the middle of the cycle and this is why the number four is about balance and harmony, associated with the colour green. Following her birthday, a few months later, she went into year five which is about communication and healing. It was during this year that she felt drawn to start recording her life story, with the well-known therapeutic effects that this can have.

I am always fascinated to see over and over again how everything in life is so interconnected. Everybody has a Life Path number but some people have come into incarnation with particularly challenging lives and this can be associated with what is called Master numbers. These are the numbers 11, 22 and 33. The double number, in fact, involves a different combination of vibrations and I have certainly observed that my clients who have these double numbers are confronted by significant challenges and can need a lot of support.

We definitely <u>know</u> what we have come into this incarnation to deal with and it is for this reason it is said that nobody is given more than they can cope with.

The pattern in Sara's life is that up to now she has been rather put down by those around her; family, school and now, work colleagues. Understanding how, through the law of attraction, we have drawn towards us the issues we are confronted with is the first step towards taking the responsibility which is needed to try and change our "troublesome thought patterns". Sara is doing meditation which will gradually clear her "muddy pot" but in the interim period the understanding of <u>how</u> the process works can be helpful. We have come into incarnation to deal with this and there are no magic wands. It is all part of soul evolvement. Understanding this doesn't make things any easier but with acceptance we can concentrate on finding the best way of living our lives. This is the path to fulfilment which can, in turn, lead to contentment. The universe is showering us with higher vibrations to quicken up the whole procedure on a planetary level.

Numerology is quite a well known subject, but I often explain to clients that everyday life is just as rich in symbolic events. A household appliance that breaks down, a run of light bulbs that go perhaps indicating an interruption in a relationship, a series of incidents associated with water since water is always involved with emotions. Or perhaps an object that is dropped and broken possibly indicating another kind of "break". Life is constantly acting as a mirror in order to help us.

Recently I have mentioned to clients how parts of the body can also be trying to tell us something. Legs and feet take us places and so not being able to get about gives us time to reflect in different ways. Shoulders can be associated with how we are carrying things, burdens for instance. We all know that when the expression "a stiff neck" is used for a person it indicates rigidity!

One of my clients is having a lot of problems with her teeth. Teeth are used to masticate. Is there something she is having trouble getting her teeth into?

Suddenly going deaf? Is there something one doesn't want to hear? Needing glasses? Is there something one doesn't want to see? And on this subject the majority of people use reading glasses as a result of unavoidable ageing. However I have reason to think that it is not completely inevitable.

It has been enlightening to hear some student meditators tell of unusual incidents when they are on the way to a session; for instance a bird that suddenly flies across the windscreen. Birds and animals do indeed come into our lives in symbolic ways. In a lovely little book *"Medicine Cards"* by Jamie Sams and David Carson published in 1988, and also in *"Birds, Divine Messengers"*, a 2006 publication by Andrea Wansbury, we discover the messages that are carried by the feathered and furry ones.

Crow is an omen of change, sees past, present and future, and merges light and darkness. Hawk is a messenger; be aware of signals in life, notice and receive them. <u>Ant</u> teaches patience, perhaps a little more trust in some life situations. <u>Mouse</u> is about scrutiny, paying attention to details.

One of my clients happened to notice how spiders seemed to be attracted to him. <u>Spider</u> brings the message "create, create, create". This client was obviously being encouraged to develop his creativity! In yet another situation a student meditator who was having trouble with many people around him, talked about deer crossing the road just in front of his car. <u>Deer</u> is about gentleness. <u>Deer</u> says "stop trying to change people, love them as they are". <u>Butterfly</u>, part of the title of this book, represents the never ending cycle of transformation in Life. I remember talking to a client on the phone who suddenly mentioned that a butterfly had just fluttered past her window, <u>not</u> by chance!

Robert, who lives locally, had come to me for a consultation. As we sat and chatted he suddenly looked through the glass door and noticed a robin that had appeared on my patio. <u>Robin</u> is about protection, asking "do you still rely on other people to protect and look after you?" Or <u>Robin</u> may be alerting us to the fact that we are not energetically protecting ourselves and others may be sapping our energy. In fact one of Robert's issues was that he had attracted a number of spirit entities. Spirit attachment is associated with "affinity", a connection between the entity and the host. As he left my cottage, by another door, the robin appeared in front of him again!

In all of these cases we have the impression that our attention is brought to focus on something that we may not notice at another moment or we observe the coincidence of two apparently different events as in the case of Robert and the robin.

From time to time it crosses my mind to offer to do a RUNE reading for a client. Runes are from ancient Scandinavian descent. They are akin, in function, to the Tarot cards, created from the secret Cabbalistic code of the Hebrew letter numbers, or the Chinese *"Book of Changes"* or I Ching which uses hexagrams. In fact one can observe that whatever the culture in which they were in use, ancient alphabets had an everyday use and also a magic, sacred and divining use. Runes usually consist of ancient meaningful glyphs, inspired by the Celtic alphabet inscribed on little flat stones. Runic symbols appeared on Viking arms and were last in current use in Iceland in the late Middle Ages. Tolkien refers to them in his famous trilogy *"The Lord of the Rings".*

They have come down to us as a contemporary Oracle that has very symbolic meanings.

On this subject *"The Book of Runes"* by Ralph Blum is a little treasure and the language he uses is delightful to read or listen to. He reminds us that with runes we are consulting an oracle "that does not give instruction as to what to do next nor does it predict in any way. Rather does it draw our attention towards hidden forces and motivations that will shape our future by their unfelt presence within each present moment." If we recognize these invisible signs they can alter our perception.

Fredrick has been a client since 2006. He has had difficulty adjusting to a break-up after 25 years of marriage. He sold his business and moved abroad to restart his life but continues to ring me from time to time for support. Recently, following a conversation about his on-going issues, I felt he might benefit from a Rune reading. I usually proceed in a simple way by shaking up the little bag of stones while thinking: "The issue is..? Where is X now?" and a Rune jumps into my hand. In this case the Rune that came up was about termination and new beginnings, "part of the Cycle of Self Transformation which progresses in five stages; death, decay, fertilization, gestation and rebirth. It is now appropriate to adapt to the demands of such a creative time for the universe supports the new growth."

These ancient Arts of divining carry messages. Are we ready to hear them? Consulting an oracle gives us the chance to actively participate in our destiny. The future is <u>not</u> predetermined and we can always change its direction. Destiny is a bit like a computer game which contains a plethora of scenarios which are played out depending on which button <u>we</u> push.

In the preface to his book, Ralph Blum begins: "The Runes as described here are healing, merciful Runes. They will do you no harm. Learn their language and they will speak to you."

Chapter 17

"Beauty is born of harmony. What is harmony? Harmony is right proportion, in other words right rhythm. And what is life? Life is the outcome of harmony and the whole creation is harmony."

Hazrat Inayat Khan

Our infinite capacity for creativity is something that everyone can explore. Perhaps we associate imagination with artists but we can be inventive in any number of everyday activities such as cooking, gardening or even having ideas!

For me it has always been music. One of my youngest memories was of being dressed up as a daffodil (Ha! it should have been an Iris!) in yellow crêpe paper and little green socks; we had to unfurl, in a group, to music which I later discovered was from Mendelssohn's "Scenes from Childhood – 'Dreaming'".

It was no doubt beneficial that my parents were musical, even though this didn't completely counterbalance the lack of close contact that I would have liked. I grew up with musical evenings where my sister and I sang songs around the piano which was played by my aunt. I also loved to hear my father singing solos as he processed around in the High Church Choir especially on feast days like Easter. This early taste for music has been carried forward into adult life and although I didn't do very much about it when the family were young I always made sure I listened to the "Festival of Nine Lessons and Carols" from King's College Cambridge every Christmas Eve. That has always been the highlight of Christmas for me.

For many years now I've sung in a choir and I'm lucky to have the advantage of being able to read music which most choirs require. In the '90s I went to hear a lovely concert of harp music played by candle-light in a castle setting and it attracted me at once. I thought, "That's just the instrument for me!" and, lo and behold, I noticed a harp day advertised in the local library soon afterwards ... "harps provided". That was how I started to play and sing with the Celtic harp. Over time I have developed a short programme of song and verse in which I present my own compositions and also arrangements of the lovely traditional folk songs when I am invited to do so locally. Music certainly seems to run in the family since two of my children have grown up to make a career out of music.

For the past few years I've been particularly interested in "Tonalis", an independent organisation, led by Michael Deason-Barrow, which operates an alternative to the standard music colleges for young people and runs courses for professionals or anybody who is interested. Michael Deason-Barrow, who comes from the background of being Head Chorister in a Cathedral, has for many years pioneered a new attitude based on the enjoyment of singing where anyone is welcome providing they can sing in tune! It is a completely innovative approach to choral singing, which is delightful. A comment by a person taking part in the last course I attended was, 'he is a national treasure!'

In *"The Secret Power of Music"* first published in 1984, David Tame maintains that music is not just an entertainment but a "literal POWER ... it is a force which affects all who hear it ... Whenever we are within an audible range of music its influence is constantly playing upon us, speeding or slowing, regularising or destabilizing our heart-beat, relaxing or jarring the nerves and thereby affecting the digestion and the rate of respiration. It affects the emotions and desires of man and goes beyond the purely intellectual and mental processes."

There is an axiom "As in music, so in life" which suggests that music tends to mould our thoughts and behaviour patterns.

In fact music may play a very important role in determining the character and direction of civilization and could thus be used or mis-used. From Ancient China to Egypt, from India to the golden age of Greece, David Tame discusses how these civilisations were very aware that there is something immensely fundamental in music.

This awareness has been preserved by the greatest musicians such as Yehudi Menuhin, the famous violinist, who, in his book *"Theme and Variations"*, stated: "music creates order out of chaos and through music a greater universal order rests upon fundamental relationships between geometrical and mathematical proportions".

The philosophy of Ancient China was that civilizations are shaped and moulded according to the quality of the music that is performed. For example, we learn that when Emperor Shun wanted to check on the state of affairs in his Kingdom he did this is in what may seem to be an extremely strange way, by testing to see if the music that was being played was at the correct pitch. The Chinese musical scale is, of course, very different to Western, European scales and in those ancient times there was no convenient standard tuning fork to use in order to tune instruments. Emperor Shun expected immorality itself to sweep the nation unless something was done to keep music at a "correct" pitch.

Confucius, the famous philosopher and teacher of ethics, held similar views which we also meet in the ancient cultures of Mesopotamia, India and Greece and it is interesting to note that the decline of music in Egypt and Greece was followed by the complete decline of their civilizations.

Another belief that was common to these civilizations is that music is able to affect and change matter itself. We have probably all heard how the walls of Jericho came "a tumbling down" suggesting that sound could have a profound effect upon society and the human psyche. The production of sound by musical instruments and singing was believed to play a powerful part on the path to enlightenment and was thought to be intimately related in some way to non physical and sacred dimensions. This cosmic sound was known to the Hindus as OM and has been transmitted over the centuries by different spiritual masters. In the final techniques that are given to my meditation students, the OM sound is always incorporated in their own individual Mantra.

The universal vibrating energies were called by the ancient Egyptians, the "Words of their Gods". To the Pythagoreans of Greece they were the "Music of the Spheres". In ancient China they were known to be the celestial energies of perfect harmony. The role of music was considered to be so vitally important that it was naturally incorporated into religious ceremony and liturgy. Gregorian plain chant, so called after St Gregory, the great disciple of St Benedict, who collected, classified and encouraged chanting in the sixth century, goes back 1,500 years and has been preserved by monks and nuns all over the world.

Both Plato and Aristotle discussed the moral effects of music and this debate persisted beyond Biblical times through to the Middle Ages and the Renaissance up to the 19th century.

It was Pythagoras who first discovered that music could be reduced to numbers and ratios. Of course this is not only true for music but also for other art forms such as architecture. Sacred geometry was incorporated into the great cathedrals and ancient buildings and one of the reasons why so many people are attracted to visiting ancient monuments is that one intuitively feels a sense of harmony. These proportions were known by the great artists and sculptors in the past such as Leonardo da Vinci, Michelangelo and the original stained glass window artists. Since the 1980s crop circles have been appearing that demonstrate principles of geometry.

The Ancient cultures thought that music was a sort of echo of cosmic sound and obeyed the same Divine Laws. Sound had the power to heal, keep people in good health and enable humanity, in its quest for universal harmony, to sing the song of the stars.

Mantras, plain chant and healing incantations have very ancient origins going back to the beginning of humanity. The rhythmic incantations of the shaman were therapeutic and many other cultures used sound as part of healing rites.

The medical use of sound is recorded on ancient Egyptian papyrus and there are many examples in the Old Testament, one of which is the way David healed King Saul's depression by playing the harp.

Nearer to us, physicians in the Renaissance and Baroque periods used "musical prescriptions" and the great composers knew that there was a relationship between sound, music and health. Handel, for instance, is reported to have declared that he didn't just want to entertain listeners but to "make them better people".

In the 19th century scientists first started to measure the physiological effects of music. All studies confirmed that the fundamental acoustic principal of resonance which affects musical instruments also affects the human body. When a sound wave enters the body all its living cells start to vibrate. Because the body has a high water percentage sound is easily carried and it acts much like a vibratory massage of each cell at an atomic and molecular level.

Sound waves are invisible but the work of two pioneers allowed us to discover, for the first time, their visible form.

The German scientist Ernst Chladni (1756–1827) was the first to show how solid objects vibrate. He scattered sand on a metal plate and made it vibrate with a violin bow. The sand formed geometrical patterns that varied with the sound frequency, the thickness of the metal plate and the size of the grains of sand.

In the 1960s Hans Jenny, a Swiss doctor and scientist, took photographs of sound waves going through liquids, powders and semi-solids such as mercury. He observed that certain frequencies were characterised by a regular, harmonious, symmetrical motif while other frequencies created a visual disorder. He wrote about patterns of recurrent rhythms throughout the living and non-living world.

Sound is movement. It is a continual oscillation, much like a pendulum going back and forth, and is produced by the movement of the atoms and molecules that make up all living matter in the universe. Sound comes from the movement of the atoms of the object whether it be as small as a mosquito or as big as a planet. We can also observe this continual oscillation or pulsation in rhythmic functions such as the beating of the heart, breathing, and the circulation of the blood. It exists in the recurrent formation of cells and tissues and throughout the universe from the cosmic systems of galaxies down to the infinitesimal world of atomic and nuclear structures. Jenny termed this field of research CYMATICS.

In *"Thought Forms"* published in 1979 by The Theosophical Publishing House, C.W. Leadbeatter shows us that music can also produce forms in super physical matter. He publishes some beautiful pictures of the effects of music when clairvoyantly observed.

Vibrational energy is transmitted through the electromagnetic fields surrounding a being (the subtle bodies) into the physical body via the chakras. Any alteration in the vibrational field affects all levels of the being. The molecules of the body initially have a harmonious relationship with each other. The principle of Sound Therapy is to restore this initial harmony via appropriate methods. All the meridian and acupuncture points have their own notes or frequencies as do the physical organs of the body. Many different therapies are based on the concept of the vibrational nature of the Universe. Gem therapy, the Bach Flower Remedies and homeopathy, to name just a few, are all based on the compatibility between the remedy frequency and the organ frequency.

Olivia Dewhurst-Maddock in *"The Book of Sound Therapy"* writes: "Healing in the 21st century will undoubtedly make more use of light, colour and sound calibrated to the vibratory rate of chemical elements, cells, organs, organisms, and states of consciousness. Composers of healing music will employ the salient frequencies of audible sound, and the range of human voices, for curative and preventative application."

Lawrence Buchan, contributing to *"Medical Marriage"*, writes an article on how the Sound Therapist must have a thorough understanding of the physio-psychological, emotional and spiritual functions of the human being.

Of course it is also important to integrate other forms of music less well known to Western ears such as the oriental scales and Indian ragas without neglecting the natural sounds in nature such as the sound of water or wind or birdsong.

In the field of the therapeutic benefits of sound on nature some studies have observed how plants grow better in fields and hothouses when recordings of flute sounds are played. Likewise cows produce more milk when music is played in the milking parlour. During the recent Tsunami some of the animals such as elephants were seen to instinctively move towards higher ground and research will perhaps reveal their ability to capture sounds or vibrations that are inaudible to man.

However, concerning the effects of modern music, some studies have been made that show how plants tend to move away from the "noisiest" forms while moving toward more harmonious sounds.

Nowadays music is accessible to everyone in many different forms but David Tame comments that, in his opinion, modern music is devoid of genuine regenerative spiritual value. In fact he concludes that much of it can even have a destructive effect on men and nations. I am certainly surprised to discover that very few of the musicians that I have "looked at" are in fact integrated people in mind, body and spirit.

However I was interested to discover that very young children, under a year old, seem to need to hear certain pieces of four-part choral music for a precise length of time every day and for a particular period of time and this brought their unbalanced endocrine glands back into balance. The music which is needed is mostly from the era of the great composers such as Bach, Handel and Mozart.

At the "Attune to Health" clinic in Morecambe, Lancashire, Gordon Dalgarno is exploring the idea that each person has their own personal pitches. He has been researching into ways of determining a person's frequency through a combination of High-Tech therapy with sound and music, Kinesiology and Emotional Freedom Techniques. In fact he is open to exploring the idea that maybe a person has more than one individual frequency. This would perhaps align with the individual Mantra that my meditation students are given which is always made up of three syllables.

A few years ago I attended a course organised by a tutor from one of the Colleges of Music who had gradually moved away from that environment as he felt that they tended to be "musical factory farms" turning out students with just skills and no deeper insights. In fact it was this course that introduced me to Tonalis that I mentioned before. These days I am able to pick up vibrational rates and I have definitely noticed that the early periods of great composers are accompanied by a higher level of consciousness. There are, of course some very gifted composers in later periods and whenever their music vibrates at a high level it is associated with a personal level of spiritual consciousness. One comes back to the same conclusion as with the therapist who cannot be separated from the therapy.

In a 1995 book by F. David Peat – *"Blackfoot Physics"* – he writes: "The more I have tried to learn about indigenous science, the more I have heard of the power of songs. Songs come to us from another world; they have their own existence and power. Songs create and renew, they heal and make whole. Songs connect us to the world of dreams, and to the visions in which healing can take place."

These lovely words from Shakespeare's *"The Merchant of Venice"* have been set to music by the celebrated English composer Ralph Vaughan Williams:

"How sweet the moonlight sleeps upon this bank!
Here will we sit and let the sounds of music creep in our ears.
Soft stillness and the night
Become the touches of sweet harmony.
Look how the floor of heaven is thick
Inlaid with patines of bright gold:
There's not the smallest orb that thou beholdst
But in his motion like an angel sings
Still quiring to the young-ey'd cherubins;
Such harmony is in immortal souls;
But whilst this muddy vesture of decay
Doth grossly close it in – we cannot hear it."

Choosing to reflect on music is by no means to overlook or to underestimate the value of other creative expressions but music has been so much part of my life that I have had the opportunity to explore this subject in more depth in order to understand its profound effects.

There are so many different ways we can develop our innate creativity. If we enjoy writing it can be very rewarding to start an autobiography. I began doing this in 1988, at a difficult time in my life. It has developed into a sort of personal journal which I update annually between Christmas and New Year. As a result of this I began to write quite a lot of poetry too – once I had managed to outgrow "the cat sat on the mat" rhyming tradition encouraged from school days!

If we have difficulty imagining a creative activity we could perhaps very simply start by looking to see what adult education classes are provided in our area. Personal resourcefulness can be so helpful in our search for integration and harmony within.

Chapter 18

"Only a human can touch the hearts and minds of another human."

Gururaj from "The Master Reflects"

Continuing our theme of an evolving species, where might our emerging butterfly begin to explore?

Perhaps we might be drawn towards a living Avatar like Mother Meera. Gururaj always said, 'keep the company of holy people, real spiritual teachers and Masters.' He explained that an Avatar is a "Bringer of Light", a pure consciousness which has embodied to teach the world and to correct imbalance at various points of the Universe. Avatars are "Beings of Light" who infuse, by their very presence and teaching, purer values of love into the darkness that exists. These Beings are in a State of equilibrium and will remain forever in this State of equilibrium. They are one with God and never lose this awareness.

Mother Meera is a very beautiful woman who was born in 1960 in a village in South India. When very young she showed herself to be an unusual child and was helped in her early years by her uncle, Mr. Reddy. She lived for some time in the Aurobindo Ashram. She now lives in Germany and attracts thousands of people to her from all over the world who come to receive DARSHAN, her silent bestowal of Grace and Light. She is recognized to be one of the several incarnations of the "Divine Mother".

I went to Germany to meet her in 1994. We gathered in a room to await her, as was the procedure, and she entered dressed in the most beautiful golden sari, accompanied by her trusted secretary and devotee Adilakshumi. She quietly sat down and anybody who wished could come up to her. She looks into your eyes and sees how she might help the person in this incarnation. This only takes her a few minutes after which a gentle nod indicates the move on to the next person. This procedure is carried out, in complete silence, for a number of evenings every week. However, nowadays Mother Meera travels overseas on a regular basis and a few times a year she visits England where more and more people attend her special gatherings. While sitting in the room in Germany I observed, for the first time, the magnificent golden aura which surrounded the upper part of her body.

From the book *"Answers"* purchased while in Germany we discover the reasons why her teaching is SILENCE. For the mind to flower it has to go beyond what it knows. All spiritual teachers say the same things. She says "people want lectures, I give them Silence." She lives in a very simple way and shows the world that transformation is normal and can take place in ordinary daily life. Asked about how the work of an Avatar differs from a self realized Guru she answers that Avatars come from the Divine while self realized persons go to the Divine. When asked how we can tell if a Guru is genuine she replies that the sign is how at peace we feel in his or her presence. The amount of help a Guru can give a disciple depends on his or her stage of development. She explains that the silent mind can receive more and that when there is restlessness people cannot feel what she is giving. People are so active and rarely sit quietly.

Mother Meera talks of the way in which family life plays an important role. It teaches us to become unselfish. She also says: "We should contribute to the world with whatever skills and gifts we have. There is no separation between 'holy' and 'worldly'. Everything is DIVINE. Everything is GOD."

Many people want to know how she offers DARSHAN and she explains: "I am looking into every corner of your Being. I am looking at everything within, where I can give healing and power. At the same time I am giving Light to every part of your Being and I am opening every part of yourself to Light."

To a certain extent Mother Meera is confirming what is being presented to us from many sources these days; if we want anything we have to "ASK" for it. We have to outgrow our conditioning, believe we live in a very abundant universe and that we are only limited by our own "thoughts". Mother Meera's teaching is the Universal Wisdom of all ages which is brought to us by all true spiritual Masters. Her book ends: "The highest serves most lovingly, the wisest listens how. The one who has SEEN gives his whole life to help others to SEE. This is the Divine way."

In a lovely comment made by Gururaj in one of his SATSANGS, which is the coming together to impart TRUTH, he says: "Don't chase after the butterflies; if you sit quietly they may alight on your shoulder."

Looking at other chinks of light appearing in our world we may hear about one of the world's great statesmen, Nelson Mandela, who, at nearly 90 years old, has recently launched a new initiative of Global Elders. Global Elders will be a group of twelve wise men and women who will work to address global problems by offering expertise and guidance. We are told that the group will "speak freely and boldly, working both publicly and behind the scenes, working wherever our help is needed." Mandela says that "this group will derive its strength not from military, political or economic power but from the independence and integrity of those that make up the group." Its members will comprise former presidents, elder statesmen, leaders, and probably Nobel Prize laureates.

Mother Meera and Nelson Mandela are, of course, exceptional people. We may feel uplifted by their example which serves to remind us that we all have a part to play in life.

It is perhaps timely to end this chapter with part of *"Desiderata"*, a 1692 manuscript found in Old Saint Paul's Church, Baltimore:

"You are a child of the universe
No less than the trees and stars
You have a right to be here.
And whether or not it is clear to you
No doubt the universe is unfolding as it should.
Therefore be at peace with God
Whatever you conceive Him to be
And whatever your labours and aspirations
In the noisy confusion of life
Keep peace with your Soul
With all its sham drudgery and broken dreams
It is still a beautiful world
Be careful. Strive to be happy."

Chapter 19

"The search for the Inner Self and God is founded on a
harmonious and continuous inner transformation,
the overcoming of personal limits, the capacity to
measure ourselves through action and practical work
and respect for all forms of life be they subtle or physical."

From the website of the
"Federation of Damanhur"

As we consider our awakening from the chrysalis state into the butterfly we can imagine that here and there groups of people are trying out different ways of organising social existence ...

Damanhur is a modern day Utopian experiment, a unique experiment in social living. It is situated in the Piedmont Alpine area of Italy. I visited this amazing place in 2002 soon after reading all about it in a book by Jeff Merrifield – *"Damanhur"* – published in 1988.

It was established in 1975 and "seems to have remained in a state of continual growth". A thousand people now live there and they have dozens of thriving businesses, their own daily newspaper, their own currency, a constitution and government, their own schools, a political movement and even their own fire department.

The founder and Spiritual Guide is Oberto Airaudi who had a vision early in his life of a "large subterranean cathedral dedicated to the cosmic evolution and spiritual rebirth of the human race". He was interested in physics, maths, music and esoteric philosophy, all subjects that he began giving lectures on. He opened a centre named after Horus, the falcon headed Egyptian Sky god. Damanhur is named after an Egyptian city, the site of a temple to Horus, sometimes called "City of Light …"

Oberto Airaudi was born in 1950 in Torino, the town associated with the shroud that was said to have surrounded Jesus' body after the crucifixion. Fifty kilometres north of Airaudi's home town is a very special area where four major synchronic lines intersect, a "supercharged" region. Airaudi, who is also known as Falco, believes that by carefully studying the flow of these energy channels "one can foresee what will happen in the future and thus modify the present". Damanhurians believe that these synchronic lines are the linchpin of their esoteric philosophy and at the heart of their esoteric research such as their knowledge of alchemy, lost Atlantean technologies, healing, divination and other concepts that are gateways through time. Falco writes about these particular energy channels being attracted to natural or man made features such as rivers, mountains and caves.

In 1977 this understanding led him, along with a dozen or so of his closest students, to move to a place called Valchiusella and in 1978 they began to work, in secret because they didn't have permission, on the Temples of Humankind. They did this without help from architects or engineers using techniques dating back to the Middle Ages. This has resulted in a five story subterranean maze of magnificent curving corridors, expansive halls where one sees soaring sculptural columns, mosaic floors, giant stained glass domes and walls adorned with occult symbology. Altars to all religions are spread throughout the labyrinth. There is a Hall of Mirrors that gives multifaceted perception and in the Hall of the Earth there are portraits of Damanahur's local history in the context of cosmic evolution. There are also a Water Hall, a Hall of Metals and a Hall of Spheres. The visitor is told about a "time cabin" in which some twenty to thirty Damanhurians claim to have travelled back to visit the Stone Age!

In 1991 the "secret" came to the attention of the Italian Authorities and was visited by the State Prosecutor along with soldiers in helicopters who were threatening to dynamite the mountain. However, once inside, the State Prosecutor was apparently overawed and vowed to do all he could to save the site. After four years it was finally given the seal of approval by the Italian government and the temples were legalised and opened up to the public in 1996. This has allowed more and more people to be able to visit what some have called the Eighth Wonder of the World!

The community is bound by common beliefs of self realisation and by a different way of life. They are very successful in trading their wonderful fabrics and luxury food to leading fashion houses and stores around the world. Their first small village of 20 people or so has given way to about 40 villages scattered throughout the valley. These form the basis of Damanhur's democratic government which is made up of one representative from each homestead and overseen by two elected "King Guides".

As far as the population is concerned, 85% of them are Italian, 57% are women, 70% work for Damanhurian businesses and 30% have jobs outside the community. From the very beginning they consciously worked to develop a sustainable Eco-society and in 2005 won an award for their achievement from the U.N. Global Human Settlement Forum. They produce half their own food, organic vegetables, olives, grains, fruit, wine, oil, honey, milk and cheese. They are proud of their energy self-sufficiency and 35% of their vehicles run on bio-diesel while another 40% are powered by methane gas.

People who go to live there have chosen to do so after carefully considering all the implications. It is pointed out that Damanhur is "no wonderland"! Being spiritual also means working hard in a practical sense in order to turn dreams into reality. Newcomers are encouraged first of all to visit, joining one of the many programmes on offer.

Music plays a very important part at Damanhur and involves the direction of choral or instrumental works. Composing for the temple is done collectively for it is pointed out that the music that is played is just as important as the stained glass or the mosaics for it fills the air with sound and gives the physical body of the temple a certain resonance. On this subject Rudolf Steiner, the Austrian philosopher and founder of Anthroposophy, believed that there is a plane of existence where music and colour are closely connected.

Damanhurians view illness as an opportunity to learn and health is thus another strand of the spiritual path. They prefer to use natural remedies but are not fanatical in their approach and conventional medicine can be used if necessary. For them health is more a way of life and they certainly understand that from a holistic point of view our environment is formed from our inner thoughts.

There is a School of Meditation and each person can choose one of the seven spiritual ways to follow. Visitors to the Temples of Humankind engage in exercises intended to widen their perceptions. This can, for instance, be through sacred dance, inner harmonizing, walking, meditation in the stone circuits or meditation with "Selfic" paintings. Visitors can also work in the art studios and take part in a full moon Ritual of the Oracle at the Open Temple.

When we investigate further into Selfica we discover that it is an "ancient science founded on one of the basic forms in the universe, the spiral. This science was known by the Egyptians, the Celts and the Arabs and has been developed at Damanhur for thirty years now. On a practical level spirals and metals can be used to concentrate and direct vital energies." Gold and silver are the best conductors but copper and brass can also be used.

I can say that visiting Damanhur is definitely a very worthwhile experience. It seemed perfectly comfortable to prepare oneself to enter their magnificent temples and the sacred dancing appeared to be so appropriate in that context. On a practical level, interpreters were freely available even when one or two of us wanted to go to a lecture on esoteric physics!

The visionary work taking place at Damanhur seems to be very timely and it is perhaps appropriate to quote their words. The vocation of Damanhur is to "link all Divinities in ONE".

Chapter 20

How like an Angel came I down
How bright are all things here!
When first among his works I did appear
O how their glory did me crown
The world resembled his ETERNITY
In which my soul did walk
And ev'ry thing that I did see
Did with me talk ...
Nothing in the world did know
But 'twas Divine.

Thomas Traherne 1637-1674

Poets such as Thomas Traherne have written immortal lines describing our descent, as babies, from the heavenly realms into this world "trailing clouds of glory".

Although the book *"Star Children"* by Georg Kühlewind, a retired Hungarian chemist, suffers a little, I feel, from the translation, it is written with great perception. He suggests how, as adults, we might learn to open our "inner eyes" so we can better understand children in general and in particular the new kind of children who have been coming down into our world for around the past 20 years. Star children are born with more active DNA. Such was a young man I spoke to a few years ago who, at the time, was living in a monastery in New Zealand because he was finding it very difficult to relate to his peers.

To enable us to understand the situation better, Georg Kühlewind explains how every child first takes hold of his or her body in a twofold way. Firstly by means of the inherited body through eye contact, smiling, standing upright, walking and speaking. This process is what he terms the GENTLE WILL. The communicative gesture of eye contact comes about through the receptive gaze of two people and stops as soon as one of them thinks of something else or when the shadow of self-centredness enters the consciousness. Many adult people feel uncomfortable with eye contact and it often does not last very long. It is interesting to note that the individual mantras given to my meditation students at the end of the three month course are "picked up" through the eyes, via a picture of them.

Later on, the awareness of SELF comes about through bodily sensation gained through touch. We now understand that when small children put things in their mouths it is part of the necessary means of exploring the world. This is a process that Kühlewind terms HARD WILL.

Gradually, by way of the nervous system, thinking and visualising develop alongside their fellow forces of knowing and feeling. Induced by the surrounding environment, speaking becomes a central means of expression. Through the soul's capacity to reflect we gradually come to knowing, perceiving and thus to consciousness. This is an active force of intelligence. The inner conscious life does not begin until children can say "I", when they become aware of being a separate individual.

According to Kühlewind a baby lives in a "holy" way. In our modern environment, dominated by the television, babies soon lose their early innocence. It is the role of fairy tales to reply to children's existential questions and they are meaningful and necessary in order to develop a healthy mind. Even as adults we can enjoy imaginary stories without, of course, fully entering into the fantasy world as children do. Our feeling life is often overtaken by rational thinking. The Pre-Raphaelite painters captured this dimension very well and many people still enjoy the fairy theme pictures that have made some contemporary artists very famous.

The work I do enables me to distinguish fundamental differences between "Star" children and other people. This is to do with levels of awareness associated with active DNA. Various sources suggest that aeons ago there was what one might term a "shut down", which consequently left us with a more limited level of awareness. On a scale that goes from 1 to 12, it has been estimated that we have been operating on a level of 2 or 3 (men at 2, women at 3!).

According to Anne Brewer, author of *"Power of Twelve"*, we are awakening again and many children now seem to be coming into the world with higher levels of awareness. However, I have observed that they are still carrying the bloodline imprints that are a hindrance for, as has already been explained, these can cause irregularities in the glandular system which in turn affect health. They also create the "muddy pot" which forms a sheath separating us from our Higher Selves.

"Star" children or "Indigo" children, as they are sometimes called, do not have this "muddy pot" and they are not carrying baggage from past lives and so the loving part of their Being is actively functioning. On the aforementioned scale these children would register at 7. They are what some go as far as to term a "new species" of human beings. Whatever the term used their presence requires us to look again, in a different way, at the needs of babies and small children.

As children grow up they are directed to fit in as quickly as possible to the world of signs and meaning around them. Child education has greatly evolved an efficient means to operate this integration as smoothly as possible. However, the modern way of life is predominantly materialistic and the more meaningful aspect is often neglected in mass education unless individual parents take initiatives. Outside of this any children that are born with "spiritual" tendencies are not taken into account in our present day "system".

When I was involved with the Playgroup Movement and tutoring on Playgroup courses, as described in Chapter 1, we discussed some very thought provoking books written by John Holt, the American educator born in 1923. The two that most influenced me were *"How Children Learn"* and *"How Children Fail"*, in which he challenges the formal methods of learning that can destroy children's natural initiative. He states that in fact we should not start to teach things until they have already been "learned". From his experience, John Holt describes how children are capable of grasping new ideas much more quickly than we give them credit for and that this natural faculty is impaired or even destroyed when the child goes to school. In his books, John

Holt analyses the strategies that children develop in order to meet or dodge the demands the adult world makes on them. He describes the difference between real and apparent learning and the ways in which schools generally fail to meet children's needs. "Educators and psychologists need to be persuaded to look at children patiently, repeatedly and respectfully and to hold off making theories and judgments about them." The honesty and respect that children demand implies profound adult self knowledge and this awareness generally leads to a greater sensitivity.

Georg Kühlewind draws our attention to the vitality and the mental energy that is, according to him, leading to more and more children being diagnosed as having an "Attention Deficit Disorder" (ADD) or "Attention Hyperactive Disorder" (AHD) when they will only pay attention to something that really interests them. This can, understandably, be very taxing for teachers who are functioning within a system of standard results and we often hear of children that are treated with drugs to calm them down.

However, in the light of the work of such people as the aforementioned authors the frustrated spiritual needs of children should be added to the long list of factors that can lead to rebelliousness, disturbed behaviour, addiction and all forms of mental and physical illness. Teaching, in general, has to move from an almost exclusive "thinking" mode to include the "feeling" dimension. We have to remember that we are essentially spiritual beings having an earthly experience. This is something that "Star" children instinctively KNOW.

There are, of course, well known examples of a different approach to education, schools that are centred on children's wellbeing, encouraging their development in an integrated way. This is the case in Waldorf schools which are based on the understanding of Rudolf Steiner, the 20th century charismatic occult philosopher, who developed Anthroposophy with its educational, agricultural and artistic applications.

Another renowned educational experiment was developed at Summerhill by A.S. Neill in 1921. In the preface to his book published in 1961 he writes: "Education should produce children who are at once individuals and community persons. The difficult child is the child who is unhappy. He is at war with himself. Summerhill is where children's unhappiness is cured and, more important, where children are reared in happiness." He declared that "all crimes, all hatreds, all wars can be reduced to unhappiness". Summerhill is carried on today by A.S. Neill's daughter.

Unfortunately, along with the Montessori schools, these alternatives to the state system are only available to a limited number.

"Star" children are coming to help us to evolve from our materialistic ways. How can we make them feel welcome in our world? What are some of the ways that we can help children in general to have a happier development?

In view of what has been said there is so much that could be done at each stage of a child's development. For instance we can encourage as much contact as possible with the natural world around us and we can also encourage an imaginative or artistic activity which involves intuition and feeling alongside thinking and is therefore healthy and therapeutic since it restores the original unity of feeling <u>and</u> thinking.

On a personal level I recall the impression of being in another world when I was taken to the High Church of my childhood. It was a lovely atmosphere with its smell of incense, candles and mystery! On another occasion, while on holiday with my parents, I will always remember the way in which a man stopped our car to draw our attention to a particular bird of prey, a buzzard. Many years later I was out for a walk with one of my children while they were still in a pram when a man stopped us and with so much enthusiasm drew our attention, once again, to a rare species of bird.

In more recent times, while visiting a big art exhibition in New York, I can recall being fascinated to see how a young mother was talking to the very young baby that she was carrying. She was describing her understanding of the pictures, as she moved about, completely oblivious to other people around her.

Being

Precious day
This holiday-holyday
Pooh playday
Happily to idle away
Dawdling, dabbling
Moodling, meandering
See the dew on the gossamer
Thread of a spider's web
Breathe in the scent of May
On a warm spring day
Be aware of the myriad of
Sights and sounds to
Awaken senses
Out of the ordinary into
The extraordinary.

Iris Sparkes

Chapter 21

*"Experiencing Christ consciousness within yourself, loving, uncondi-
tionally, that which you are as you exist and abide in your reality at
this point in time creates the resonance within your being that attracts
the identical Essence within the opposite body of soul energy. Your Soul
Mate will manifest in physicality, as a natural progression, and merge
with your energy and you with it. And as you merge together closer
and closer and drink more and more of one another's cups you become
ONE and you become one another's strength and one another's love.
As this occurs you experience what is called enlightenment."*

St Germain "Twin Souls and Soul Mates"

We are beginning to understand the meaning of "soul mates" and
"twin souls". This is the subject of the book by St Germain.
As the Karmic family links are released we can experience a gradual
re-grouping into "soul mate" groups and the recognition of the exact
identical male/female frequency vibration known as "twin flames". This
has not been heard about much up to now since it has been necessary
to reach a certain stage of evolvement and soul mate grouping can only
happen once individual people have attained complete integration of
mind, body and spirit.

Christ consciousness is not confined to the Christian religious
understanding but to universal understanding that has to emerge far
beyond all individual religions.

Sometimes we catch glimpses of this twin flame/soul relationship and it changes us forever. However, until we understand the deep
implications of this experience it can be difficult to come to terms with

since we can attach current romantic ideas around it all rather than seeing things as being for our nourishment and realising how they may contribute to the raising of the consciousness of the whole planet. Maybe those fairy tales of the prince and princess living happily ever after are all that have remained as ideals embedded in the memory of our collective unconscious...

Some lovely words were written a hundred years ago by the Victorian novelist, Marie Corelli, who has left us an unforgettable book called *"The Life Everlasting"*. This has been described by people as being the greatest love story of all times in which she describes the trials and tribulations of souls prior to the re-uniting of male and female energies:

> *"Love has been born in the Soul and of the Soul. It must be a dual flame, that is to say it must find its counterpart in another Soul which is its ordained mate, before it can fulfil its higher needs. Then like two wings moved by the same soaring impulse it assists the WILL and carries it to the highest heaven. Through its force life is generated and preserved. Without it, life escapes to other places to find its love again. Nothing is perfect nothing is lasting without the light and fire of this dual flame ... What is heaven? – A state of perfect happiness. What's happiness? – the immortal union of two souls in one, creatures of God's eternal light, partaking each other's thoughts, bestowing upon each other the renewal of joy, and creating loveliness in form and action by their mutual sympathy and tenderness. Age cannot touch them – death has no meaning for them. Life palpitates through them and warms them with colour and glory as the sunshine warms and reddens the petals of the rose - they grow beyond mortality and are immune from all disaster – they are a world in themselves involuntarily creating other worlds as they pass from one phase to another of production and fruition."*

What a glimpse this is of what might await us as we ponder on life way beyond the caterpillar stage!

Life emerges from silent <u>inner</u> processes similar to the endocrine glandular changes now taking place and transformation of this order is rather unlikely to be associated with any <u>exterior</u> cosmetic techniques! All of this confirms the rise in consciousness suggested by Dr. David Hawkins. There is undoubtedly a movement that is drawing us to evolve.

We may like to muse on these words of Guillaume Apollinaire:

"Come to the edge he said
They said, 'we are afraid'
Come to the edge he said
They came
He pushed them
... and they FLEW."

Shall we descend from the mountain top and see how all of this understanding might be playing itself out in our lives at present as more and more of us may indeed be preparing to reunite in this very special way after aeons and aeons of soul evolvement?

In *"Cords that Cannot be Broken"*, published in 1997, Judith Merville describes her encounters as she travelled up and down the country to meet people who believe that their destiny has been to meet their Twin Soul in this lifetime.

However, before going any further, it is important to define the term "Twin Soul" since it is often used in a rather general way. In fact there are different kinds of soul mates.

There is what is known as a COMPANION SOUL MATE where a good relationship has been built upon over many lifetimes so that in this present lifetime it is possible to have a very compatible experience. There is also what is known as a KARMIC SOUL MATE where it has been important to fall in love and be together perhaps because of some unfinished business.

TWIN SOULS/FLAMES are, of course, soul mates but unlike the situation formerly described, TWIN SOULS have always been inextricably part of each other. One could talk of an individual soul that became dual so as to evolve and to learn by contrast. The destiny of this soul is to find ONENESS. This is so well explained in *"God I Am"* by Peter O. Erbe.

Going back to Judith Merville, she describes a wide variety of different Twin Soul experiences. For instance, the way in which two people can teach one another important lessons even if, in some cases, this can be a painful experience. In other situations it seems to be necessary to remain separate in order to allow soul growth. Some soul mates may not need to be together physically whereas for others, on the contrary, being together can increase their strengths and talents. They can also be of the same sex and it goes without saying that for soul mates physical age is immaterial!

The common thread that seems to run through encounters with a Twin Soul is the instant recognition of a momentous occasion, the feeling that there is no need to "get to know" one another since there is an authentic communication from the outset. To meet one's Twin Soul is to experience the strongest possible link between human beings.

One of the most well known Spiritual Masters, Jesus, is equally one of the most enigmatic since we know very little about his adult life until he appears as a "preacher" accomplishing miracles. Various theories have been suggested and some of them explore the relationship that could have existed between Jesus and Mary Magdalene. In *"Mary Magdalene, Beloved Disciple"*, published in 2005, Clysta Kinstler raises the possibility that Mary Magdalene may have been secretly married to Jesus and that as a Magdalene she would in fact have been a High Priestess.

Following meticulous research, Laurence Gardner, in his *"Grail"* books, also discusses the relationship between Jesus and Mary Magdalene and the possibility that there might have been bloodline descendants.

I personally feel that they may well have had what we might call a Twin Soul union. In this eventuality, could there be a link between this possible union and the miracles achieved by the Master Jesus as recorded in the New Testament? It is likely that once Twin Souls have both reached complete integration, union of energies, through resonance, may lead to an enhanced healing ability...

At this present stage very few souls are actually <u>ready</u> to live together. Perhaps we get glimpses and then there is a sort of "soul quickening" but it is nonetheless clear that union cannot take place until both souls have reached the same level of evolvement. Helping people to release "baggage" can, in many circumstances, be the very first step in the direction towards greater opportunities.

Judith Merville describes the union of Twin Souls as "a love that cannot be contained. It's a spiritual condition which is eternal." This will, however, express itself according to individual situations.

Lena is still a young woman hoping to have a family yet, following the break-up with a Twin Soul encounter, she has been unsettled in other relationships and draws back when a commitment is required. Lena first contacted me about three years ago concerning a health issue and mentioned this particular relationship that had disturbed her. As has already been said, I am able to determine the nature of particular relationships in the same way as I do other parts of my work. In Lena's case I was able to say that she had had a Twin Soul meeting. I hadn't needed to contact her for more than 18 months but I wasn't really surprised when she telephoned concerning her ongoing relationship at a time when I was writing on the subject of Twin Souls for this book. The person that she had had the Twin Soul encounter with was now married to another person but he felt the need to send her an e-mail from time to time. In her effort to reconcile the situation she feels that this occasional "how are you?" contact can help to settle her enough to get enjoyment from her current relationship. She thinks that she may even be able to move ahead and buy a joint property with her present partner. Lena obviously needed to talk all of this through since she had come to realize that sitting alone and daydreaming was not very helpful. Perhaps this is indeed a solution in her case but the answer will only come after she has tried it. Another option would have been to openly discuss things with her partner. However, not many people are ready to "embrace" the freedom that this implies in their relationship.

As described in the early chapters of this book the powerful encounter that I personally had and that completely changed the direction of my life wasn't recognized at the time as a Twin Soul experience and happened at a much later stage of my life when I, fortunately, wasn't faced with the situation that now confronts Lena.

Judith Merville explains that the Twin Soul encounter doesn't necessarily bring about a relationship break-up unless, of course, this is already crumbling anyway. On the contrary, the current relationship could be very important for us at that stage. She goes on to remind us that it doesn't serve anyone to go searching to the ends of the earth for a Twin Soul. It is much more worthwhile to endeavour to discover our life purpose and to make the best of our abilities.

William Blake, the great English poet, painter, engraver and mystic wrote these lovely lines...

> "... *He who kisses the joy as it flies*
> *Lives in eternity's sunrise ...*"

Epilogue

"SATYAM, SHIVAM, SUNDARAM" – "BEING, KNOWLEDGE, BLISS"

I was quite impressed to read the above words quoted in a 2003 book about Prince Charles entitled *"Radical Prince"*. I use these words at the end of meditation every day. I believe we are very fortunate to have a man of his vision who often uses speeches to speak his truth. In 1991, to mark the 150th anniversary of the Royal College of Psychiatrists, he reminded the audience of their motto "Let Wisdom Guide" and, in conclusion, said: 'More needs thee the Divine than the physician ... I believe that the most urgent need for Western man is to discover the divine element in his Being.'

We are "created to create"; such are the comments in the most advanced reading now available, *"The Knowledge Book"* accessible on the Internet. It is well known that this modern technology has been given to us to help us to find the truth for ourselves. Of course, it also allows, by contrast, much that is undesirable but we also have to learn discrimination ...

However, through *"The Knowledge Book"*, the need is expressed to go beyond all religions and it reminds us that Divine Authorities are not religious authorities. Religions developed to try and unify the world but this has not really been a success and has brought a lot of division and hatred. People are still killing each other in the name of God! The teaching of certain religions has degenerated through misinterpretation. Through *"The Knowledge Book"* we learn that the world is an evolution laboratory for the phenomenon of METAMORPHOSIS. We are experiencing a silent but profound resurrection. The person who becomes <u>conscious</u> can grasp the truth more comprehensively. The physical constitution will, in time, regenerate itself and overcome sickness. It is not a medical matter; it is a natural process. We are moving to an age of knowledge, an age in which consciousness will be enlightenment through the path of Science and Learning. Prophethood has come to an end. No-one can intercede for anyone else. In this understanding women will have a foremost place in the walk. From a little book published as far back as 1946 on the teaching of the sage Swami Vivekananda we can read:

"The Living God is within you and you are building churches and temples and believing all sorts of imaginary nonsense. The only God to worship is the human soul in the human body – man is the Taj Mahal of temples."

Again, from *"Conversations with God"*: *"If you don't go within you go without."*

The young New Zealand client, already mentioned, who was living in a monastery at the time, suggested I might like to read a book first published in 1953 called *"Divine Healing of Mind and Body"*. This book is also known as *"The Jesus Lectures"* through channelled material to Murdo Macdonald-Bayne. These lectures were only attended by a small group of people in Johannesburg, South Africa. Immediately one notices that not once are the words Christian or Christianity ever used. Some lovely thoughts are expressed ...

"When you begin to understand that the Christ of God dwells within you, you will not look outside for Him. I have told you not to gaze too long upon the sin of the world, which too many are preaching about. How can you see the Christ if you are forever gazing at sin? Love dwells in every living soul. Love much and I shall do my work through you. Love is of God; good and evil are of man's mind. The pure in heart see God in everyone. Seek not revenge for that which is in your heart will befall you also. Personalities must fade out of your minds before you can see the Reality of Christ."

In conclusion, if we observe nature in general we see that evolution is a natural ongoing process. The innate change from caterpillar into butterfly is a metaphor that can serve to remind us of what is possible for, as living organisms, we are all made of atoms and molecules that are constantly engaged in this process of renewal. Science tells us that in one year 98% of our cells will have regenerated! Is it perhaps due to our blinkered perception that there are still "illness, ailments and disease" all around us?

As quoted in *"Ageless Body Timeless Mind"* by Deepak Chopra, thousands of years ago the greatest of Indian sages, Shankara, declared: 'People grow old and die because they see others grow old and die.' He goes on to say that he had come to realise that he wasn't seeing old people at all, but sick people. He said the ageing process was learned, and that the bonds of conditioning could be broken.

We have seen that self-healing <u>is</u> possible and that correct meditation and spiritual practices are aids in releasing the troublesome "thought forms" that are hampering this natural process.

Shakespeare seems to have had profound insight when he gave Caliban some immortal lines in *"The Tempest"*:

"The clouds methought would open and show riches ready to drop upon me, that, when I wak'd, I cried to dream again."

"Beyond all Illness, Ailments and Disease" all our dreams can become reality, for the caterpillar does become the beautiful butterfly, spreads its wings and flies ...

"The road goes ever on and on
Down from the door where it began
Now far ahead the Road has gone,
And I must follow, if I can,
Pursuing it with eager feet,
Until it joins some larger way,
Where many paths and errands meet,
And whither then? I cannot say."

Bilbo Baggins – as he sets forth for his great adventure
in "Lord of the Rings" by J.R.R. Tolkien.

MELROSE BOOKS

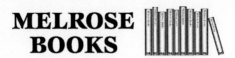

If you enjoyed this book you may also like:

One In A Million

Chrissie Daplyn

Chrissie Daplyn has been a Christian since the age of twelve, but she could never have dreamt how much Brian and herself would need the support of God.

She was diagnosed with a rare type of cancer called Pseudomyxoma Peritonei, an illness that would usually prove to be fatal. Her faith and beliefs played a very important role in allowing her to come to terms with her ailment. 'We had to believe God for a miracle and at the same time ascertain if there was any research being done that would afford me some medical help.'

One In A Million is a true-life story portraying Chrissie Daplyn's experiences from the time when she first found out about her illness to her first experience at the gym, an activity advised by her surgeon. Each tale is told with great honesty and her descriptions of the tough times combined with her humour and joy for life are both entertaining and interesting.

Size: 210 mm x 148 mm	Pages: 79	
Binding: A5 Format Paperback	ISBN: 978-1-906050-10-8	£9.99

Bring it On

Gio Terni & Mandy Paterson

For anyone seeking to walk the spiritual path, Bring It On provides a fascinating guide to every step of the journey. Gio Terni and Mandy Paterson are two pathwalkers who have dedicated their lives to helping others. Now, follow Gio as he courageously embarks upon the classic Heroes' Journey, of self-discovery embracing a fascinating mix of teaching, personal growth, Qabala, channeling, auras, the Harmonic Concordance, tarot, past life regressions, Buddhism, the Hebrew Letters, psychologically interesting courses, grief, loss and addiction.

Bring It On is a comprehensive guide for the seeker of Inner Wisdom and will be compulsive reading for anyone curious about or contemplating stepping into a more connected, vibrant way of life.

Size: 234 mm x 156 mm	Pages: 192	
Binding: Royal Octavo Hardback	ISBN: 978-1-906050-86-3	£13.99

A Handful of Seeds

Helen M. Downs

Introducing readers to new age spirituality; An essential self help guide with illustrations. Our view of this earth and our reality has evolved over time and is still changing. There are those who are right "into" the New Age and/or ancient traditions and have intricate knowledge and understanding of specialized fields in energy, tone, vibration, spirituality and healing. This book is not for them! This book will not be likely to tell them anything they have not already heard, seen, done or worked with.

A Handful of Seeds is intended for their friend, the skeptic, who silently wonders what weird and wacky flight of fancy they are on now.

This is a fantastic and intriguing guide for any one who wants to learn about spirituality!

Size: 234 mm x 156 mm	Pages: 96	
Binding: Royal Octavo Hardback	ISBN: 978-1-906561-02-4	£12.99

St Thomas' Place, Ely, Cambridgeshire CB7 4GG, UK

www.melrosebooks.com sales@melrosebooks.com